SPECIAL PUBLICATION 125

CONTROL OF RISK

A Guide to the Systematic Management of Risk from Construction

Patrick S Godfrey   BSc CEng ACGI MICE FInst Pet
Sir William Halcrow and Partners Ltd

CONSTRUCTION INDUSTRY RESEARCH AND INFORMATION ASSOCIATION
© 1996, ALL RIGHTS RESERVED
6 STOREY'S GATE, WESTMINSTER, LONDON, SW1P 3AU
TELEPHONE 0171 222 8891 FACSIMILE 0171 222 1708
E-MAIL SWITCHBOARD @ CIRIA.ORG.UK

Godfrey, P.S.

Control of Risk
A Guide to the Systematic Management of Risk
from Construction

*Construction Industry Research
and Information Association*
Special Publication 125

ISBN 0 86017 441 7

Published by CIRIA
6 Storey's Gate
Westminster
London SW1P 3AU

CLASSIFICATION
AVAILABILITY - Unrestricted
CONTENT - Advice/Guidance
STATUS - Committee guided
USER - General

"No construction project is risk free.

Risk can be managed, minimised,

shared, transferred*, or accepted.

It cannot be ignored."

Sir Michael Latham, 1994.

* Note although risk can be transferred, legal duties and responsibilities cannot. See Section 5.6.

ABOUT THIS GUIDE

INTRODUCTION

For too long the construction industry, its clients and the public have suffered the painful consequences of failure to manage risk, exemplified in many major projects by long disputes and out-of-control schedules and cost budgets. A recent, joint government-industry report, *Constructing the Team* by Sir Michael Latham (1994), concludes that real savings of up to 30 percent of construction costs are possible with a will to change. Addressing the issue of risk is key. This Guide is therefore a timely introduction to the processes of systematic risk management, designed to increase the likelihood of successful project completion with subsequent positive effects on project performance.

READERSHIP

The Guide is tailored to the needs of clients responsible for the development, procurement and management of construction projects and services and with some knowledge of the construction process. If you are a first time client, start by reading the companion CIRIA publication *Planning to Build?*.

PURPOSE AND SCOPE

Systematic risk management is a tool to help you control risks from your construction projects. The Guide is designed to assist you in this process by:

- introducing a simple, practical method of identifying, assessing, monitoring and managing risk from construction in an informed and structured way
- providing advice on how to develop and implement a risk control strategy that is appropriate to your business
- identifying when and how to seek and evaluate specialist advice in assessing your risks.

The methods described can be adapted to any type of construction project and tailored to control all types of risk. A full treatment of health, safety and environmental risks, however, is beyond the scope of this Guide. These are specialised subjects with their own laws and practices in which you may need expert advice.

THE STRUCTURE OF THIS GUIDE

The Guide is structured for ease of use.

For a concise overview of the concept, issues and benefits of systematic risk management, read Sections 1 and 2.

For detailed guidance on how to start the process, read Sections 3-6 in conjunction with Tool Boxes 1 and 2, which together take you step by step through the basic techniques.

Finally, Tool Boxes 3 and 4 unveil some advanced analytical methods, to give an appreciation of the range of approaches available, without going into the detail.

Section 2.1

Bibliography

"Maps" of the Guide and Tool Boxes are provided for ease of reference. The arrow symbols in the left margin are used throughout the Guide where a cross-reference to another Section is advised. The information symbols refer to further reading in the bibliography.

THE LANGUAGE OF RISK

The Guide deliberately uses everyday language for ease of understanding and defines the term "risk" in the commonplace way as the chance of an adverse event. Bear in mind, however, that in other contexts, such as cultural, legal or mathematical, the meaning of terms such as "hazard" and "risk" may differ.

BASIS OF GUIDANCE

The Guide is based on a research study of clients' awareness and attitudes to construction risk undertaken for CIRIA between November 1993 and September 1995. The study objectives, approach and findings are presented in the project report, *Risk from Construction: Preparation of a Clients Guide*, available from CIRIA.

ACKNOWLEDGEMENTS

The research and preparation of this Guide were commissioned by CIRIA and undertaken by Sir William Halcrow and Partners Ltd, in association with Professor Peter Thompson, AMEC Professor of Engineering Project Management, University of Manchester Institute of Science and Technology, Professor Philip Capper, Masons Professor of Construction Law, King's College, University of London and Laing Technology Group Ltd. The principal author was Patrick Godfrey and the work was managed by Stuart Withycombe, both of Sir William Halcrow and Partners Ltd. Editorial assistance was provided by Susan Pacey. The design concept and layout of the Guide was created with the assistance of Trevor Good of Halcrow Fox. The project was funded by the CIRIA Core Programme, the Department of the Environment and the Health and Safety Executive.

The work was overseen by a steering group comprising:

P J Duffy (chairman)	W S Atkins Property Services, Essex
W S Charles-Jones	London Underground Ltd
W B Critchley	Laing Management Ltd
Professor R Flanagan	University of Reading
J A Goodwin	The Builders' Accident Insurance Ltd
M James	Health and Safety Executive
C Norris	TBV Schal
D F Richmond-Coggan	Mouchel Management Ltd
A W Rogers	Manser Associates
G Sampson (retired)	Department of the Environment
J Ioannou (successor)	Department of the Environment
J Steele	Meica Ltd
C N Strickland	Greycoat plc
A Jackson-Robbins (Research Manager)	CIRIA

Corresponding members:

S Barnes	Department of Transport
C L Leighton	Union Railways Ltd
E A Minogue	McKenna and Co
P B Woodhead	Department of the Environment
D F Yuill	Galliford Midlands

The valuable contributions of the ten "clients" interviewed in confidence as part of this study and those of the large number of representatives from the major professional bodies who reviewed an early draft of the Guide are gratefully acknowledged. Their comments represented a broad spectrum of views which helped steer the development of the Guide.

THE GUIDE

SECTION 4

WHO SHOULD DO YOUR RISK ASSESSMENT?

An overview of the skills and qualities that make an effective risk management team, and the key role of an impartial facilitator.

SECTION 5

ESSENTIAL ISSUES

An exploration of major risk considerations from the project planning stage onwards.

SECTION 6

HOW TO SUCCEED

A summary of points to keep in mind as you develop your risk management system throughout the project cycle.

THE RISK MANAGER'S TOOL BOXES

1   INTRODUCING SYSTEMATIC RISK MANAGEMENT

1.1 A SYSTEMATIC APPROACH TO RISK MANAGEMENT

Everyone should be concerned with risk management, because risk and uncertainty with potentially damaging consequences are inherent in all construction projects. The success or failure of your project and your business depends on your approach to risk.

Risk management is not new. Traditionally it has been applied *instinctively* with risks remaining implicit and managed by judgement informed by experience. The *systematic* approach makes your risks explicit, formally describing them and making them easier to manage. In other words, systematic risk management is a management tool, which for best results requires practical experience and training in the use of the techniques. Once learnt, it supports you in your decision-making and informs your instinctive judgement.

In brief, systematic risk management helps you

- identify, assess and rank risks making your risks explicit
- focus on the major risks from your project
- make informed decisions on your provision for adversity, e.g. mitigation measures
- minimise potential damage should the worst happen
- control the uncertain aspects of construction projects
- clarify and formalise your role and the roles of others in the risk management process

and, perhaps most importantly

- identify your opportunities to enhance project performance.

Although you can never remove all uncertainties, systematic risk management improves the chances of your project being completed on time, within budget and to your required quality, with proper provision for safety and environmental issues.

1.2 WHAT IS RISK?

Risk, defined as the chance of an adverse event, depends on circumstances.

The impact of a risk can be measured as the likelihood of a specific unwanted event and its unwanted consequences or loss:

$$\text{impact of risk} = \text{likelihood} \times \text{consequence}$$

1.3 THE MEASUREMENT OF RISK

The *likelihood*, or more technically, the probability of an adverse event, is usually expressed in terms of the number of such events expected to occur in a year; if the event is expected once every 10 years, it will have a probability of occurrence of 0.1 per year. (Time is not the only measure of likelihood; for example, the likelihood of production defects in steel bars might be measured per kilometre of bar produced.)

The *consequence* of an adverse event, sometimes called damage, is often expressed in monetary terms. However, it is more appropriate in the case of fatalities or serious delays to use other performance measures.

The impact of *risk*, as the combination (multiple) of *likelihood* and *consequence*, will usually be expressed in £s per year in an annual budget. However, the methods proposed in the Guide work equally well for other units of measurement, as long as the units are applied consistently throughout the assessment.

Consider carefully events which, though unlikely, are potentially catastrophic. The risk may appear insignificant, yet disaster *can* happen. If the consequences are unacceptable, then the risk must be avoided or at least mitigated, e.g. through insurance against fire or flood.

1.4 HAZARD AND RISK

Distinguish between *hazard* and risk. A hazard has the potential to do harm or cause a loss, but the degree of risk from the hazard depends also on the circumstances. For example, petrol is a hazardous substance but the risk from it depends on:

- its nature (it is inflammable)
- how it is used
- how it is controlled
- who is exposed
- what is being done.

In many hazardous situations, risks can be reduced to acceptable levels by the quality of risk management applied.

E.g. The impact of risk

> A large housing development was to be constructed close to an old fireworks factory. Arsenic, discovered only after work had begun, needed to be removed to meet stringent environmental standards. Great extra costs were incurred owing to the complexity of the clean-up, resulting in delays and changes to the main contract. The impact of the risk could have been reduced by a pre-acquisition land contamination survey.

1.5 WHAT RISKS DO YOU FACE?

Risks arising from construction may be categorised in three different ways:

- risk to *activity,* e.g. delay in completion
- risk to *health and safety,* e.g. personal injury
- risk to *environment,* e.g. pollution.

Cost is the common link; that is the money, time and effort required to control these risks to acceptable levels. However, risks faced by clients are wider than those normally associated with construction. By and large:

- risk to your construction project is not the same as risk from the project to your business although in practice both are closely related
- risk management focused solely on your project is of limited benefit
- actions to control risk to your projects, and to your business from the projects, may differ
- transfer of all the construction risk to the construction industry means transfer of control of the risk. Projects are then managed without regard to your business requirements which may change during the life cycle of the project
- the interests of the construction industry in your project are concentrated on the construction activities; your interests are for the whole life of the project, beyond completion of construction.

5.6 Safety risk

Consider the distinction between risks which affect your project and those which affect your business. Risks are specific to a project, interactive and sometimes cumulative: they all affect cost and benefit. A wide range of risks arising from construction projects may threaten your business. Some of the key risk sources are listed below.

E.g. Sources of risk

SOURCES OF RISK TO YOUR BUSINESS FROM YOUR CONSTRUCTION PROJECTS	
Heading	**Change and Uncertainty in or due to:**
Political	government policy, public opinion, change in ideology, dogma, legislation, disorder (war, terrorism, riots)
Environmental	contaminated land or pollution liability, nuisance (e.g. noise), permissions, public opinion, internal/corporate policy, environmental law or regulations or practice or "impact" requirements
Planning	permission requirements, policy and practice, land use, socio-economic impacts, public opinion
Market	demand (forecasts), competition, obsolescence, customer satisfaction, fashion
Economic	Treasury policy, taxation, cost inflation, interest rates, exchange rates
Financial	bankruptcy, margins, insurance, risk share
Natural	unforeseen ground conditions, weather, earthquake, fire or explosion, archaeological discovery
Project	definition, procurement strategy, performance requirements, standards, leadership, organisation (maturity, commitment, competence and experience), planning and quality control, programme, labour and resources, communications and culture
Technical	design adequacy, operational efficiency, reliability
Human	error, incompetence, ignorance, tiredness, communication ability, culture, work in the dark or at night
Criminal	lack of security, vandalism, theft, fraud, corruption
Safety	regulations (e.g. CDM, Health and Safety at Work), hazardous substances (COSSH), collisions, collapse, flooding, fire and explosion
The above list is extensive but not complete. Tool Box 1 will help you identify other risk sources.	

Bibliography

Toolbox 1. Risk identification techniques

Assess which of the above risks:

- could have serious impact on the success of your project
- are increased by your project
- are reduced by your project
- create other opportunities.

For example, a drainage project might reduce the risk of flooding but increase the risk of bankruptcy whilst also providing an opportunity to increase the car parking space available for your customers.

1.6 EXPECTING THE UNEXPECTED

It is impossible to identify *all* risks. To believe you have done so is counter-productive to risk management and dangerous. Always expect the unexpected. Systematic risk management will help you cope with the unforeseen as well as minimise damage caused by identified problems.

1.7 OPPORTUNITIES, RISK AND VALUE

Risk and opportunity go hand in hand. For this reason, there is usually a commercial benefit, or "added value", from risk control measures you take. For example, you may decide to provide a hoist instead of a set of ladders on site to reduce the *risk* of people falling. The added value of this risk control measure may be that the hoist increases people's mobility and as a result their productivity. Consideration of potential opportunities arising from your risk control activities calls for little extra effort during the risk management process and can aid your decision-making by giving you a more complete picture of likely outcomes. It is useful to note that the techniques used in the application of systematic risk management are similar to those used in the management process known as *value management*, outputs from each being closely linked and inter dependent. Benefits, both in terms of time and cost savings and improved effectiveness, can be achieved by closely co-ordinating inputs to these two activities. For an introduction to the processes of systematic value management, refer to the companion CIRIA publication *Value Management in UK Practice*.

 Bibliography

1.8 OWNERSHIP OF RISK

The term "ownership of risk" has a variety of meanings which include:

- having a stake in the benefit or harm that may arise from the activity that leads to the risk
- responsibility for the risk
- accountability for the control of risk
- financial responsibility for the whole or part of the harm arising from the risk should it materialise.

When a risk materialises, the harm that occurs is seldom restricted to one organisation or person. Some are direct "stakeholders" and some indirect. Whereas the former may include your own organisation, your team, your contractor, subcontractors and his suppliers, insurance companies and financiers, the latter may include the public and your customers, their insurance companies and professional advisors. Deciding who "owns" risk is sometimes difficult. Risk management will help you address this issue.

1.9 TRUE COST OF RISK

 Bibliography

The true cost of risk can be much higher than is apparent. Much of it can be indirect and uninsured as illustrated in Figure 1 below drawn from a case study presented in *The Cost of Accidents at Work* by the Health and Safety Executive. This study demonstrated that the uninsured cost of health and safety risk can be eleven times the direct costs on a construction site. The risk issues therefore can be much more complex than appears at first sight. It is helpful to keep the task of identifying the cost of risk simple and focus on:

- what is important
- actions which control risk.

Figure 1 Accident iceberg - the hidden cost of accidents

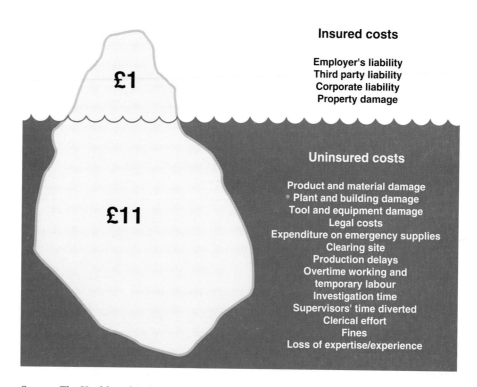

Insured costs

Employer's liability
Third party liability
Corporate liability
Property damage

£1

Uninsured costs

Product and material damage
Plant and building damage
Tool and equipment damage
Legal costs
Expenditure on emergency supplies
Clearing site
Production delays
Overtime working and temporary labour
Investigation time
Supervisors' time diverted
Clerical effort
Fines
Loss of expertise/experience

£11

Source: The Health and Safety Executive, 1993, The Cost of Accidents at Work.

1.10 COMPLACENCY IS DANGEROUS

Organisations experienced in executing construction projects naturally develop procedures that respond to the risks that they have encountered. They can be particularly vulnerable, however, to new risks such as those resulting from change or innovation. Change may also render some of their risk control practices obsolete.

1.11 TRANSFER AND SPREADING OF RISK

If you attempt to transfer risk to others but resist the transfer of control of that risk, it will generally lead to an overall increase in the cost of risk. It can also mean that you end up paying not only for the transfer but also for the consequences of the risk if it materialises. Moreover, you may add the legal costs of sorting out the responsibility, which can escalate the consequences even further.

Some large companies which can afford to absorb losses actively seek high risk/high profit projects in areas where they are highly experienced and can gain a strong competitive advantage. Smaller companies may prefer to spread the risk to reduce its overall effect, at a lower return on their investment, because they cannot afford the higher risk. Good management of risks does not necessarily imply a *reduction* in risk.

E.g. Spreading risks

> If oil exploration wells cost £1 million and have a 1:10 chance of striking oil, a small oil company may prefer to take a 10% share in each of ten wells at £100,000 per well rather than wholly financing one. Thereby the company increases its probability of success but reduces the return on its capital if successful.

1.12 MORE HARM THAN GOOD

Some risk reducing measures can do more harm than good. For example, the provision of marginally effective risk control measures may create a false sense of security which increases the risk. A costly risk management measure may prevent more cost-effective measures being provided elsewhere. Moreover, what may be a risk reduction measure for your project may cause increased risk to your business.

E.g. More harm than good

> The risks of road traffic accidents along a section of motorway road works may be reduced by speed limits, warning signs, speed cameras, and coning off motorway lanes so that there is a buffer between construction staff and passing traffic. However, the traffic disruption and delay that such measures may cause could lead to many motorists finding alternative routes, thereby increasing traffic load on less safe roads and the overall potential for accidents.

1.13 RISK TO YOUR INVESTMENT

When you invest money in your project, you accept risks to achieve a desired benefit from the project. At the outset, uncertainties in the prediction of cost and benefit generate a range of likely outcomes, as shown in Figure 2. Risk management will help you determine and control this range. The base case represents the best prediction which can be made in the early stages of project definition. Construction risks can increase the cost, delay completion and, consequently, delay payback and reduce the forecast benefit.

Whilst rigorous risk assessment and management has its greatest impact during the pre-project period prior to project approval, like design, risk management is an iterative process and offers greater overall benefit when applied throughout the project life cycle.

Figure 2 Project cash flow diagram showing the escalating influence of the cost of risk over the life of the project.

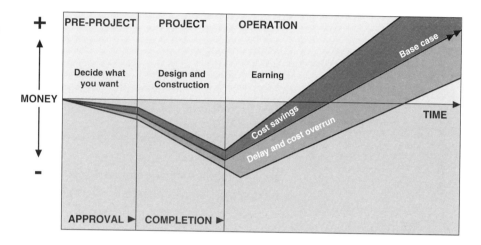

1.14 A SPRINGBOARD FOR ACTION

Good management of the risks faced by your business is essential to its success. Risks arise from uncertainty in any factor which affects the achievement of the project objectives. The greater the uncertainty, the more flexible the response and the greater the effort devoted to risk management must be.

Systematic risk management is not an end in itself, but a process to help you identify and focus on priorities, make informed decisions and take appropriate action. You can effectively plan and monitor your procurement strategy once you have identified your major risks.

5.8 Procurement strategy

2 WHAT ARE THE BENEFITS OF SYSTEMATIC RISK MANAGEMENT?

2.1 BETTER CONTROL OF UNCERTAINTY

There are high levels of uncertainty at the outset of many projects. Any feasibility study necessarily contains many assumptions. Systematic risk management helps you control that uncertainty because it:

- identifies and questions which assumptions could most affect the success of your project
- concentrates attention on actions to control the risk
- assesses the cost benefit of such actions.

2.2 GREATER CONFIDENCE

Confidence comes from certainty, but in the absence of such certainty, your confidence can be increased by knowing where the uncertainty is greatest, how extensive that uncertainty is and what the potential consequences are.

2.3 BETTER BRIEFING

The application of systematic risk management at the outset *clarifies your objectives* and helps refine your project brief, both essential to your success. When setting your project objectives, systematic risk management helps you recognise the importance of any constraints you may set and assess their impact on the project.

E.g. Recognising the importance of project constraints

> A project for the construction of 100km of large diameter pipeline in a remote location with many logistical problems required the deployment of an excessive amount of expensive resources to meet an onerous construction programme. It transpired that the imposition of the early completion date was not an operational requirement but was to meet a convenient date for the government minister to open the project. This artificial constraint magnified the risks inherent in the project and added considerably to the project costs.

One of the greatest causes of uncertainty at the start of a project is the problem of producing the brief, i.e. defining what is required. *The ideal project brief springs from your objective and is appropriate, succinct and clear.*

Many conflicts are caused by a change in brief; this may be inevitable, if so, you can anticipate it and introduce measures to control its consequences.

Devising the brief is generally made easier by the *visualisation* of the finished project using simple drawings or models. Risk can be reduced by this low-cost method.

E.g. Change due to weakness in visualisation

> A school had decided to convert a class room into a home economics room. Only after installation of the cookers was it realised the degree to which their layout presented a hazard to the children. They had to be moved resulting in additional work for which the contractor increased his lump sum price substantially. The school had to open on time. If the local fire officer and the teaching staff had been able to visualise what was being provided then the problem could have been avoided. Valuable funds that could have been used to provide new text books and equipment were, instead, absorbed by the additional construction costs.

It is a frequent "catch" that the source of finance depends on a well-developed project, and a well-developed project depends on the source of finance. At this early stage, the likelihood of a successful outcome is greatly enhanced by your participation in the iterative and concurrent processes of design and risk management.

2.4 IMPROVED AND INFORMED DECISION-MAKING

Systematic risk management techniques can help you appreciate the risks associated with your project. Decisions can therefore be based on an objective, detailed and realistic assessment of the situation, taking into account the possible outcomes of alternative courses of action. Moreover, with a systematic approach, where risk analyses are taken at regular intervals during your project, you can monitor both your risk exposure and the effectiveness of your risk control measures. Decisions are then informed by the feedback.

E.g. Uninformed decision-making

> A client appointed a space planner to advise on the refurbishment of an existing building to allow for new use. Consultations during the development of the design led to a change in strategy and a requirement for an entirely new building. The space planner proved incapable, in spite of hiring a small sub-consultant architect, of providing the necessary design and management input for the revised building construction. Whilst the limitations of the space planner's experience had been known at the time of his initial appointment, they had not been reviewed in the light of the new requirements for the design. The project finally overran by 40% in cost and 50% in time due principally to this oversight.

2.5 CONCENTRATION OF RESOURCES ON WHAT MATTERS

Systematic risk management entails the early prioritisation of risks. Therefore, you do not need contingency plans to cover almost every eventuality. As a result, you can ensure that your limited resources are concentrated on the major risks to achieve maximum effect, i.e. the areas where the greatest savings can be achieved and/or where there is maximum risk exposure.

E.g. Plan for your objective

> A large European company wanted to develop a chocolate factory in the UK and derive benefit from the Christmas market but wished to withhold knowledge of the development from competitors for as long as possible. A short design and construct programme was crucial to the success of the project. Two key constraints were identified; obtaining necessary planning approvals and completion by early November. A fast-track approach was adopted which focused on meeting the project programme by offering incentives to both the designer and contractor for timely completion adding cost to the project. The project objectives were met; the chocolates reached the shops in good time for Christmas where initial sales justified the increase in construction cost.

2.6 TEAM COMMUNICATION AND MOTIVATION

The methodical consideration of risk by your project team helps ensure evaluation from different perspectives. From the start of the project, you, the client, and your project team have opportunities to air your views and ideas and to listen to those of others, thus improving your understanding of each other's concerns and motivations.

 4.1 Your risk management team

Depending on the size, complexity and value of the project, it is usually beneficial to create a specialist risk management team from members of your project team and, possibly, external advisors. Having communicated your project objectives, you can use risk management techniques to help you and your project team, through your risk management team, identify, understand, define and rank risks. The process allows feedback from individuals on their experience of previous projects, which you need to consider objectively. A major benefit is that team motivation and confidence are enhanced by the shared understanding of the project and its associated risks.

2.7 PROVISION FOR RISK AT MINIMUM COST

By clarifying and making your risks explicit, systematic risk management helps reduce the cost of risk. Lack of clarity in the recognition or acceptance of risk is a risk in itself that will tend to magnify the overall cost of risk. The start of a project presents the greatest opportunity to avert disaster by providing for risk at minimum cost. As the project progresses, options are irrevocably closed by decisions taken. A systematic approach which focuses on risk issues at an early stage is more likely to have high cost benefit and is therefore recommended from inception, through successive project phases, to completion and beyond.

E.g. An early risk assessment

Preliminary plans were being prepared for a development involving a canal crossing the site of a deep excavation. Confidence in the continued operation of the canal was important for the success of the project. Two major risks to the temporary support of the canal were identified by risk assessment:

- toppling of the very high cranes, required for the deep excavation, onto the suspended canal, and
- leakage from the canal softening the foundations for the temporary supports.

On the first, a stepped approach to excavation was used, reducing the height of the cranes and avoiding the risk altogether. This change would have been precluded once the original plans had been passed. On the second, one of the assessment team recalled a damp patch in a tunnel below the canal. The scope of the site investigation was modified to establish the extent of the problem, and the risk of extra cost and disruption to the contract resulting from unforeseen ground conditions was reduced.

2.8 REALISTIC ESTIMATES

Systematic risk management encourages you to itemise and quantify risks and to consider risk containment and risk reduction policies. Instead of relying on a single value project cost estimate, you produce a distribution of project costs, with confidence levels, making the estimating process realistic because it recognises the uncertainties that exist.

2.9 BETTER ACCOUNTABILITY

 3.5 The deliverable, a risk register

Systematic risk management offers a means of improving accountability in your risk control by helping to identify and assign responsibility for risk management or ownership. When an adverse event materialises, damage, not least for example to your credibility, can occur if you are unable to demonstrate that the full impact of the risk was anticipated and accepted. This is particularly the case with minor risks. The ability to point to a risk register that has identified and described the risk can avoid considerable investigation costs as well as inevitable loss of confidence.

2.10 PROTECTION OF YOUR BALANCE SHEET

If you undertake more than one project at a time, systematic risk management of each project can allow you to lay off risks from one project against another, ensuring that your overall balance sheet is not overburdened with high or low risk schemes.

3   THE RISK MANAGEMENT PROCESS

3.1 THE RISK MANAGEMENT PROCESS

4.1 Your risk management team

Tool Boxes

The risk management processes described in this Section, together with the basic techniques presented in the Risk Manager's Tool Boxes 1 and 2 at the end of this Guide, are designed to enable you to undertake an initial qualitative assessment of your risks. The systematic process is illustrated in Figure 3. A risk assessment of this kind is iterative and should involve several members of a project team, lending their range of skills and experience to the process.

However, you may find it useful to start on your own.

Begin with a subject with which you are familiar. This will help you to develop and refine the process. As you read this Section, you may find it useful to refer to Tool Boxes 1 and 2 where the tools described can be adjusted to fit your purposes. If, however, you conclude you need further quantification of your risks, some methods of more detailed assessment and analysis are introduced in Tool Boxes 3 and 4, with which you may need expert help.

3.2 YOU, THE CLIENT, ARE THE KEY

You, the client, are the key to a successful project. Regardless of your construction experience, you have detailed knowledge of your own business and know what you want to achieve and why. As the person commissioning the project, your input is vital. So, when it comes to planning your scheme, start by defining in as much detail as possible:

- your objectives, and
- your constraints.

3.3 WHEN TO USE SYSTEMATIC RISK MANAGEMENT

5.1 Cost Benefit

Figure 1

Consider using systematic risk management in the following circumstances:

- when you have serious concerns that something could go wrong
- when you are introducing technical or organisational novelty or change
- when there are specific targets that must be met
- when there is an unexpected new development in a project
- at major decision points or points of change in the life cycle of a project
- to help resolve particular issues, e.g. procurement strategy, contingency allowances
- where cost uncertainty is great at the time of commitment to substantial expenditure (cost uncertainties can often be hidden, e.g. large provisional sums; dispute resolution cost and litigation; weather, geotechnical, archaeological and contamination risks)

- when required to do so by funders, e.g. HM Treasury, financiers or insurers
- when consequences can be catastrophic but the likelihood so remote that the event of concern is outside of normal experience.

You may also use the methods described here to identify inefficient or ineffective risk control measures. You may have too much risk protection or what you have may be costing more than it is worth.

Figure 3   Ten steps to risk control, described in Section 3, to identify, assess, mitigate and monitor your risks.

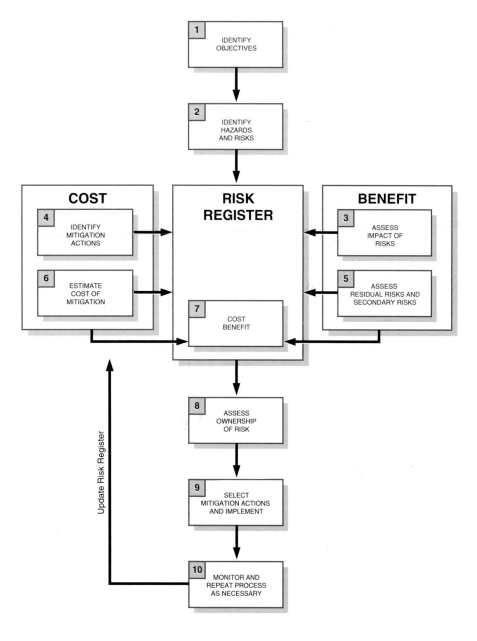

3.4 THE FIRST STEP

The first step is to summarise the subject and objective of your risk assessment in a few sentences. This summary will help you restrict the scope of your assessment to manageable proportions and keep a clear focus. The exercise can be repeated for other subjects. Examples of topics you might address include:

 1.2 What is risk?

- risk to the balance sheet from your project
- risk of delay to commissioning the plant
- risk of a fatality, injury or lost time on your site
- risk of a director being prosecuted (e.g. owing to release of a hazardous substance).

E.g. Risk control

 Figure 3

The following summarises the methods of risk control described in this section.

TEN KEY STEPS TO RISK CONTROL

1.   Identify objective of assessment
2.   Identify hazards and risks
3.   Assess risks (likelihood and consequences)
4.   Identify mitigation actions
5.   Assess residual risks (including secondary risks)
6.   Estimate cost of mitigation
7.   Estimate cost benefit of mitigation
8.   Consider ownership of risks
9.   Decide what to do: select and implement beneficial mitigation actions
10. Monitor and repeat process by updating register as necessary

Explanation of the steps

The principle	The example
A hazard has potential for harm.	Fire is a hazard.
Likelihood and consequence of risk depend on circumstances surrounding the hazard.	Where is the fire? Who is exposed? Where is the fire station? When might the fire occur?
Mitigation actions change circumstances. The primary cost of mitigation is the cost of the actions.	Fitting a sprinkler system is a mitigation action.
Residual risk is the risk that remains after mitigation has been implemented.	The likelihood of a fire is unchanged, but the consequences are reduced because the fire is less likely to spread if a sprinkler system is fitted.
Residual risk includes secondary risks. The cost of secondary risks should be included in a cost benefit assessment.	If the sprinkler system could be accidentally activated, causing damage, this is a secondary risk.

Ownership of risk

(a) Who is responsible for controlling the risk? Who is accountable?	Usually the client, unless he delegates it to others.
(b) Who pays for the risk if it materialises?	Usually the client; also possibly: contractor, designer, insurers and customers, staff or emergency services if harmed by the fire.

3.5 THE DELIVERABLE, A RISK REGISTER

Tables 2 and 3
Tool Box 2

3.6 HAZARD AND RISK IDENTIFICATION

5.2 Continuous improvement

1.5 What risks do you face?

Tool Box 1 Risk Identification
Techniques

4.1 Your risk management
team

The outcome of this type of risk assessment is usually presented as a *risk register*. It is important to record the process of production of the register by keeping copies of its stages of assembly, but, as it develops, retain in the register only the parts that continue to matter. Condensing the register to a concise form helps you clarify issues and reach sound conclusions.

Unless the hazard or the risk is identified, it cannot be consciously managed. Spending time identifying risks to your objective and presenting them in a form that helps you to control them is therefore crucial.

Focus on the subject of the assessment, for example by:

- studying the drawings and draft brief for the project
- visiting the construction site or receiving a report on progress
- reading the environmental impact report
- reviewing performance records.

The question you need to address is:

- What can go wrong?

Methods which make this process effective are introduced in Tool Box 1. They include:

- what can go wrong analysis
- free and structured brainstorming
- prompt lists
- structured interviews
- hindsight reviews, case examples or emergency procedures.

At this stage, avoid making judgements about the importance of a risk. It may be that on its own it is minor but in combination it is serious. The identification of an implausible risk may stimulate identification of an obscure but important risk. At this stage do not worry about duplication. It is easily eliminated as you assemble the risk register.

As you go through the risk identification process, it becomes less productive. Select and use only the methods in the Tool Box which are appropriate to your circumstances. As one method becomes sterile, it may feed another which revitalises the process. For example, initial brainstorming may focus attention on an area where structured interviews are needed.

Make sure you involve colleagues who understand the issues you are addressing. At each stage of the risk management process, ask yourself if you have involved the right people. This critical issue is explored in Section 4.

You do not need to restrict yourself to conventional methods if you are inclined to experiment. Black humour or games with simulation programmes can generate good ideas. If the risk identification process is made interesting and enjoyable, it is more productive.

E.g. Simulation can help to identify risks

> A baggage handling system was being designed to transfer bags in an airport. An interactive computer graphics programme had been produced to demonstrate that the overall desired performance would be achieved with the specified components. The programme included a facility to block components at whim. It was entertaining for team members to see how quickly the handling system could be brought to a state of "gridlock". As a result of the game, minor alterations were made to the layout of the baggage handling system, providing major improvements to mishandling rates.

Having written down your risks, the next task is to describe them as concisely and specifically as possible in a logical sequence. It will help to relate the risk to the source of harm, i.e. the hazard. Organise the risks by type: e.g. those involving underestimates of cost or possibly crimes (theft or vandalism). The list becomes the *risk description* and its *detail*, as shown in the risk register, Tables 2 and 3, in Tool Box 2.

It is important now to eliminate duplication or overlapping in your risk descriptions. You only need to capture the nub of the risk to plan ahead.

3.7 RISK ASSESSMENT

The objective of the first stage of risk assessment is to decide, by calculating the impact of risk, which risks need managing and which are to be left to fortune. In the first instance aim only to get an approximate assessment. Some issues are bound to be unclear. Acquiring more information through advanced assessment techniques may be necessary.

What is particular to a project rather than what is common to all similar projects often pinpoints the risk most in need of management action. The commonplace is normally dealt with as a matter of course, although complacency needs to be avoided.

3.8 LIKELIHOOD OF RISK

 1.3 The measurement of risk

To measure likelihood of risk, refer to Table 4 in Tool Box 2. Consider what is the period of concern for your objective and round up or down to the nearest multiple of 10. Take this value to be the nominal value of time T and use it to set the scale of likelihood in Table 4. For example, if the design life of the project is 60 years, take T as 1 in 100 years. The other qualitative descriptions in the table apply to periods that vary by factors of ten from that value. Consider then the likely frequency of the risk event and relate this to Table 4. This task can be difficult and is more easily tackled if you have some facts to hand. For example, knowing that about 4000 people a year are killed on the roads and that the population is about 55 million will help you estimate the likelihood of a typical person being killed.

3.9 CONSEQUENCE OF RISK

1.3 The measurement of risk

The importance of risk is related to the severity of its consequence, or outcome, should it materialise. In practice a range of outcomes can usually be anticipated which may be equated to the qualitative scale of consequences provided in Table 5 in Tool Box 2. Where you require an estimate of risk cost, you will need to decide on a nominal value V that meets the classification "serious" for your particular circumstances.

3.10 RISK MITIGATION

Table 3
Tool Box 2

Actions to control risks are usually referred to as risk mitigation. If you understand the hazard (risk source) and the circumstances leading to its consequence and likelihood, you can identify more easily your mitigation options, using similar techniques to those used initially to identify risks. Include your mitigation options in your risk register. Some hazards sometimes referred to as "soft" hazards, such as lack of communication or incompatibility of systems, defy assessment. Even if the impact of risk is difficult to estimate, the identification of effective mitigation actions can still be very useful.

The benefit of mitigation is a reduction in either the consequence or the likelihood of risk or both. You can identify the residual risk by assessing the change in each component and the resulting impact. Beware of secondary risks, i.e. those that are caused by the mitigation action. Take them into account when considering the residual risk.

Each mitigation option can often be used to control a variety of risks, so consider the accumulated benefits of mitigation and compare them with the cost of implementation. Bear in mind that the cost of implementation can escalate with delay and reduce the cost benefit significantly.

1.8 Ownership of risk

Identify accountability for the mitigation action including review of its feasibility and establishment of an implementation plan if required.

3.11 GENERAL ASSUMPTIONS

Risk control is not intended to be a design or construction or procedural check. It is normal for the following assumptions to be included in the risk register to avoid misunderstandings:

- all systems, facilities and structures are designed and constructed in such a way that they are fit for their purpose
- all systems, facilities and structures will be adequately maintained
- adequate training, supervision and quality control will be provided at all stages
- construction, commissioning and operations are carried out by appropriately trained and skilled personnel
- all designs and activities will comply with applicable laws, regulations, standards and recommended practices.

After completing the risk register, it is useful to check that these assumptions are justified.

4 WHO SHOULD DO YOUR RISK ASSESSMENT?

4.1 YOUR RISK MANAGEMENT TEAM

Systematic risk management requires the combined wisdom and experience of business and construction specialists and cannot be done by one executive alone. Assembling the right team to manage your risks demands a serious investment of considered thought, time and effort.

The chances are that the ideal risk management team comprises you and your senior managers as well as external professionals. The challenge is to create a cohesive group with the right balance of skills to operate like a vital organ within your project team. This is not an easy task.

Risks are seen differently by promoters, bankers, insurers, architects, engineers, contractors, accountants, lawyers, marketeers, managers and end-users. Accordingly, individuals' attitudes and experience may lead to differences in their understanding of the project objectives; inevitably this affects how they identify, evaluate and manage potential risks.

Remember that perhaps the biggest risk of all is lack of communication between parties.

4.2 USE A FACILITATOR

Every risk management team needs a *facilitator*, who may or may not be an existing member of your project team. Proficient and experienced enough to take on this key role, ideally the facilitator:

- is expert in all relevant risk management techniques, to help command the confidence of all parties involved
- understands technical issues relevant to your project
- understands commercial issues relevant to your project
- has good management skills
- has good communication skills.

The facilitator leads the risk management process, chairs meetings and generally helps you get the full benefits of systematic risk management. Appointing a facilitator from outside your organisation usually gives the role and the person an air of impartiality and therefore greater credibility among risk management team members.

4.3 CRITERIA FOR SELECTING YOUR RISK MANAGEMENT TEAM

Your facilitator can assist you in selecting your risk management team, which ideally:

- aims to be objective
- has a good understanding of the project's objectives and constraints
- includes a representative from each of the key disciplines involved
- is as small as possible, to facilitate decision-making (remember that a small team, through interviews and other research techniques, will be able to obtain further relevant information where necessary)
- is flexible (as the project proceeds, membership of the team should change to reflect changes in the level of input from particular disciplines)
- is inquisitive and capable of lateral thinking; team members should be able to think about more than the obvious
- includes good team players
- includes clear communicators.

The selection of your risk management team needs to reflect the individuals' ability to identify the risks and strategies to manage them. It is the quality of the decisions taken that provides the ability to manage risks, not the size of the balance sheet available to accept the risks.

5   ESSENTIAL ISSUES

5.1 COST BENEFIT

3.10 Risk mitigation

Systematic risk management helps control risks, but costs more to undertake than simply taking a decision on the basis of instinct. Assessing the cost benefit of risk mitigation (refer Section 3) helps you select the right approach, either systematic or instinct based.

Figure 4 shows that initially an *instinctive* approach will give you the highest cost benefit. Instinctive decisions may cost nothing in time or control effort. Sometimes such decisions can be wrong, thus the benefits are not always positive. The cost benefit of adopting a *systematic* approach tends to obey a law of diminishing returns; costs escalate to accommodate greater accuracy and greater detail. If you already have an effective risk management system in place, then its cost benefit is likely to be close to the optimum. Systematic methods tend to be beneficial in areas of potentially high risk exposure or where circumstances limit the use of extrapolation of past experience, as in new ventures or response to change. To help determine whether a systematic approach is appropriate for your project, consider the examples listed in Section 3.3.

3.3 When to use systematic risk management

Figure 4 The cost benefit of systematic risk control

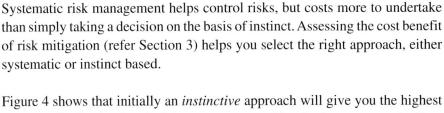

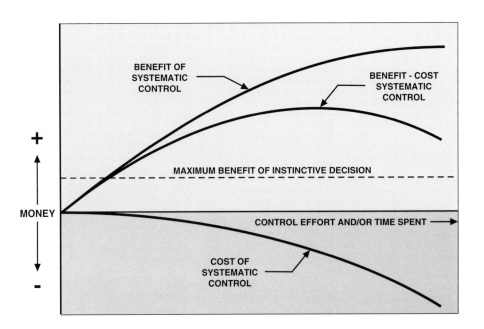

Experience is the key in your selection method: the more risk management you practise, the more likely you are to know when to use it and when to stop.

5.2 CONTINUOUS IMPROVEMENT

As the project progresses and becomes defined, you need to review and reassess the risks. The first risk assessment can be used to feed subsequent assessments, keeping the tasks to a minimum. You can monitor the outcome of risk assessment on one project and feed it back into those that follow by means of hindsight review. This helps lessons to be learned and effort to be concentrated on what is different.

5.3 IMPORTANCE OF EXTREMES

One of the major constraints on accurate estimates of cost benefit from risk control is limited data and our ability to use it to predict the future. Remember that awareness of the possible *extremes of risks* is much more important than accuracy of details. This is because damage caused by extremes can often be crucial: major failure might bankrupt a company, whereas a minor failure might be absorbed painlessly in a contingency.

5.4 PLANNING AHEAD

A golden rule in systematic risk management is "plan ahead". A skeleton *risk management* plan with prompt words (shown below) will assist you.

E.g. Skeleton risk management plan

Sections of plan	Risk prompt words
Introduction	Background, basic information, e.g. location, previous risk management, contact names, telephone and fax numbers, business contacts, organisations, who matters, your constraints and business objectives
Scope of risk management	Cost, programme, health, safety, environment, to whom, from what, objectives, time frames, project brief, what it is all about
Methods	Identification, brain storming, interviewing, data collection, risk registers, mitigation actions, assessment, likelihood, consequence, importance, values, acceptability, quantification of cost benefit
Activity plan	Project activities, key decisions, risk management tasks
Risk assessment management	Project organisation, risk management team members, facilitator, reporting, specialists, analysts
Programme	Project programme, logic, milestones, decision dates, risk activity dates, reporting dates, bar charts
Confidentiality	Agree the rules at the start, blame-free reporting
Deliverables	Risk register, assessment/analysis results, trees (decision, fault or event), contingency estimates, risk mitigation action plans, further analysis, data collection plan, testing plan, observational approach plan

Quality of planning is key when you are considering the risks you face; therefore:

- focus on risk issues alone
- be succinct in your descriptions
- avoid duplication
- note down revisions and dates
- avoid generating volumes of paper: it is counter-productive.

A good risk plan is an integral part of the project plan.

5.5 RISK MANAGEMENT IN THE PROJECT PROGRAMME

In many cases, risks materialise in the form of disruption or delay to the project programme. The effects may be cumulative. The preparation of a realistic programme is an early requirement of any approach to risk identification. Risk management may then be considered as part of your continuous and structured planning cycle. All uncertainties, particularly those which cause delay, will affect *investment* in the project.

A project is successful if it fulfils its purpose and meets or exceeds its objectives regarding:

- construction time, cost/earnings performance and quality
- environmental safeguards, and
- health and safety issues.

As your project progresses, your risk exposure and the relative importance of various risks alter. Monitoring of risks and planning of responses are therefore a necessary part of the iterative risk management process.

E.g. Phases of a generalised construction project

 1.5 What risks do you face?

Project phase	Sub-phase	Typical risk issues
Pre-project	Concept/feasibility Statement of requirements Technical specification	Political, Environmental, Regulatory

Project	Front end design
	
	Detailed design
	
	Procurement
	
	Construction
	
	Commissioning
		Contractual:
		  - procurement
		  - design
		  - method of
		    construction
		
		Regulatory:
		  - safety
		  - public nuisance
		  - environment

Post-project	Operation Maintenance Decommissioning and abandonment	Product market, Operations, Contamination

Note: The phasing of risk issues can vary from that stated.

5.6 SAFETY RISK

The construction industry's safety record is poor compared with industry generally. The safety record in maintenance and repair work is as bad. Accidents on your construction projects may adversely affect your business, whether you are contractually responsible or not. Even if you transfer the responsibility for safety management, you still have a legal responsibility in the event of an accident.

i   Bibliography

The Construction (Design and Management) Regulations which came into force in March 1995 place duties on all those involved in construction work, including clients, designers and contractors. These Regulations require you to appoint a Planning Supervisor during the design phase and a Principal Contractor during the construction phase to co-ordinate health and safety matters on your project. Guidelines published by the Health and Safety Executive further describe your legal duties under these Regulations and how you can obtain more information.

The assessment of safety risk is a specialist area for which methods such as ALARP (as low as reasonably practical) have been developed for evaluation of safety issues. The Tool Boxes can be used with some modifications to help in this task. However, it is beyond the scope of this Guide to describe these methods in detail.

The specialist areas of health and safety, and environmental risk, with their own laws and practices, are subjects on which you may require expert advice to help you evaluate.

5.7 OPTIONS IN RESPONDING TO RISK

Once risks have been identified and assessed, you have a number of possible responses:

- risk retention (or risk absorption)
- risk reduction (including observational approach)
- risk transfer
- risk avoidance
- risk removal.

In *risk retention*, the benefits to be gained from accepting the risk have to be balanced against the costs. For example, in motor insurance policies, many motorists will bear the cost of the first £100 of any loss in return for a reduction in their insurance premiums; they weigh up the probability (and likely cost) of loss or damage against the reduced premium.

Risks can be *reduced*, for example, by taking physical measures to protect property, staff and the general public. You can also introduce education and training to alert project staff to potential risks, or appoint a design checker to reduce the possibility of design faults going undetected.

The *observational approach* means monitoring the symptoms of the risk and taking action to keep the outcome within acceptable limits. In some circumstances, an observational approach can result in impressive savings, provided effective monitoring is put in place. With this method, you adjust your risk management plans and actions in response to feedback from monitoring risks that develop over time. Assessment of many issues including human behaviour, durability and technical performance can take this form.

For success, there are various important constraints that must be met. These include an ability to control the risk in practice and provision for adequate response times and resources in the event of the risk materialising. Without proper provision in your procurement strategy you should not use the observational approach.

E.g.   Observational approach

> A land slip was taking place, slowly moving about one hundred houses towards the sea. Based on the information available at the time when cracks began to appear, an appropriate remedial scheme would have been far too expensive. The only option appeared to be progressive remediation and eventual abandonment with a blight on the value of the properties and a reduction in the quality of life of the residents. However, an observational risk management plan was adopted. Instrumentation was installed with partial ground stabilisation measures. Observations were correlated to movement until the problem was so well understood that it was possible to relate the movement to the stabilisation provided and to the rainfall in the year. Most of the uncertainties had been eliminated. Stabilisation was completed at a fraction of the original forecast cost for such a scheme. Once the remediation was finalised, the houses recovered their market value and residents kept their homes.

Transferring a risk does not usually eliminate it, but passes it on to somebody else, as in insurance.

Some risks can be *avoided* by having contingency plans which normally imply a refusal to accept the risk, perhaps by using an exemption clause in a contract.

Risk removal means eliminating risks by removing particular hazards from the project so that they no longer pose a threat.

5.8 PROCUREMENT STRATEGY

Few clients, if any, have in-house all the resources necessary to undertake their construction projects. In any event, to do so might limit access to external experience. So procurement of external skills, such as design and construction capability, is essential. There are many different procurement strategies available which allocate risks in different ways. Having a reasonable perception of the risks you face will help you define your procurement strategy, taking the following issues into consideration:

- Realistically, how well can the project be defined at the outset or how much will need to be developed as information emerges during design, construction, commissioning and operation?
- Have you the authority and determination to accept the compromises that result from decisions being frozen at milestone dates or do you want the flexibility to change at later dates?
- How well can your needs be described in terms of measurable performance parameters or standard specifications alone?
- Will the project involve a wide variety of specialists?
- Is the project of a scale that will stretch the resources of organisations you need to involve?

- What is the relative importance, to your objectives, of timing of completions, minimising cost and cost certainty?
- How important are construction quality, maintenance cost and repair disruption, to your overall objective?

5.9 CONTRACTS ARE TOOLS FOR MANAGING RISKS

Your contracts for professional services and construction are the framework for you to implement your procurement strategy. It is necessary to decide the strategy before selecting a form of contract for its implementation.

A fundamental reason for a contract is to manage and allocate risk.

Construction projects often proceed despite high degrees of uncertainty. Participants can be remarkably willing to move forward with no certainty as to:

- design solutions
- the eventual scope of the works
- the time realistically needed to complete the works
- outturn costs
- scope of sub-contract works
- terms of contract.

In these circumstances, contracts determine the consequences of risks you identify. They are your opportunity to determine the practical and financial consequences of matters which are uncertain when the contract is agreed. As well as reducing uncertainty, contract documents provide mechanisms for action, provided that those mechanisms are clearly defined. All too often, uncertainties are left unaddressed in documents and conflicting assumptions are carried into the project by different participants.

Contracts are adaptable tools and not ends in themselves. A construction contract must specify:

- what you, the client, have to do
- what the contractor has to do
- by what dates these various tasks have to be carried out, and
- pre-defined mechanisms for payment.

Contractual frameworks are changing rapidly. Technological advance has to be integrated into construction projects, across disciplines well beyond those of the traditional construction supervisory team: architect or engineer. Despite the many interfaces, the whole has to be managed within a single coherent legal and contractual framework. Remember that:

- the *contractual framework* is the key to managing legal risk
- the contractual framework for the construction phase needs to be *realistic and appropriate* to the objectives and constraints of your project.

Table 1

Bibliography

Table 1 provides some introductory guidance on contract strategy selection. However, this table is a simple overview for a limited range of risks and the appropriateness of the contract is often not as clear cut as indicated. For more detailed guidance on contract strategy, consult the companion CIRIA publication *Planning to Build?*.

5.10 CONTINGENCY MANAGEMENT

Make sure you provide realistic contingencies when planning your project, since you, as the client, are ultimately accountable for risks and outcomes. Keep a close eye on the management of these contingencies throughout the project cycle.

Contingencies are required to provide additional resources for management to respond to uncertainties or unexpected events. They are an essential provision in all but the simplest construction projects and are of three basic types:

T3.6 Cost contingency analysis

- tolerance in the specification
- float in the programme
- money in the budget.

The greater the risk, the greater the need for appropriate contingencies. The circumstances governing their use are frequently interactive and, in many cases, are initiated by delay. Consequently, they are likely to be used when replanning the works and frequently involve a trade-off between float, money, and tolerance to meet changed circumstances.

Reassess your contingencies continuously throughout the project cycle. As the project progresses, revise the allocation of contingencies to accommodate change.

Where separate contingencies are allocated to cover specific major risks, identify them in the estimate and define clearly who has authority for their use. Usually this is the project or contract manager, who needs to exercise sound and disciplined judgement and yet act quickly in uncertain circumstances.

5.11 DISPUTE RESOLUTION

No construction project is free of risk and very few are free from conflict over who pays when the risk materialises. The explicit identification of risk helps to reduce conflict, particularly if you involve all parties in the risk management process and share its outcome. The practicality of this approach will depend on your contracting strategy.

Unresolved conflict within your project team can be a major source of risk to many of your objectives. It may jeopardise the efficient management of other risks. Your approach to dispute resolution is crucial, since it will have a significant influence on the cost of the risk to you when it materialises.

A protracted dispute is a lost cause for everybody with an interest in the success of the project.

Table 1 Summary of advantages and disadvantages of contract strategies

SUMMARY OF ADVANTAGES AND DISADVANTAGES OF CONTRACT STRATEGIES						
Project Objectives		**Appropriateness of Contract Strategy in Meeting Project Objectives**				
Parameter	**Objective**	**Traditional***	**Construction Management***	**Management Contracting***	**Design & Manage***	**Design & Build***
Timing	Early Completion	○	●	●	●	●
Cost	Price Certainty before construction starts	●	○	○	○	●
Quality	Prestige level in design and construction	●	●	●	○	○
Variations	Avoid prohibitive cost of change	●	●	●	●	○
Complexity	Technically advanced or highly complex building	○	●	●	○	○
Responsibility	Single contractual link for project execution	○	○	○	●	●
Professional Responsibility	Need for design team to report to client	●	●	●	○	○
Risk Avoidance	Desire to transfer complete risk	○	○	○	○	●
Damage Recovery	Ability to recover costs directly from the contractor	●	○	●	●	●
Buildability	Contractor input to economic construction to benefit client	○	●	●	●	○

Note: This table is for guidance only. Generally the appropriateness of the contract is not as clear cut as indicated

Key: ● appropriate
       ○ not appropriate

* For an explanation of these terms, see the companion CIRIA publication *Planning to Build?*

Source: CUP Guidance note 36, 1992, Contract Strategy Selection for Major Projects.

 Bibliography

6   HOW TO SUCCEED

6.1 UNIQUENESS OF YOUR RISKS

Your risks are a blend unique to your business. For this reason, your approach to risk management needs to be tailor-made.

6.2 MAKE YOUR RISKS EXPLICIT

You need to identify your risks, i.e. make them explicit, so that you can decide on your priorities both in terms of the risks and of practical control measures.

6.3 FOCUS ON RISKS THAT MATTER

Major risks can end in catastrophe and must be avoided, whereas you can leave some minor risks to look after themselves provided they are not allowed to escalate. Between these two extremes are other risks which you need to control and which you can clarify through risk assessment techniques. The process helps you focus on the cost benefit of risk control measures.

6.4 APPLY YOUR JUDGEMENT

Systematic risk management *serves* your judgement; it does not replace it. Although systematic methods used to support an instinctive approach tend to cost more to implement than an instinctive approach alone, the combination is more effective.

6.5 STAY INVOLVED

Your input and continuous involvement in the risk management process is essential, since all the risks to your business are yours. Remember that the risk from your project to your business is often larger than the risk to the project alone.

6.6 THE RIGHT TEAM

In systematic risk management, it is the *quality* of the appointed team rather than the man-hours spent that counts. Communication among all members, up, down and across the line is crucial.

6.7 SPECIAL RISKS

Health, safety and environmental risks are special cases. With expert assistance, you can adapt the Tool Boxes to help you control these types of risks.

6.8 TIPS TO REMEMBER

- Always expect the unexpected. It is impossible to identify all risks.
- Risk assessment does not need to be exact to be useful. The level of uncertainty can indicate a need for action.
- The truth is a great ally. Say the things that need to be said when assessing your risks.
- The golden rule is plan ahead. Your greatest potential benefit from risk management is at the beginning of a project.
- Generally, the cost of risk transfer is greatest at the outset and reduces as uncertainty diminishes with progress.
- Plan for emergencies.
- The biggest hazard of all is usually lack of communication.
- The most unpredictable hazard is people.

6.9 LEARN STEP BY STEP

The implementation of systematic risk management is like learning to drive. You have to practise to learn, but if you are over-ambitious too early, you will come to grief. Tips for starting out include:

- ensure you have visible support from the top of your organisation
- begin on a trial basis, using techniques in this Guide to support your usual procedures
- monitor your progress and the effectiveness of your methods
- allow enough time for the benefits of the trial to be realised in practice.

6.10 FOCUS ON SUCCESS

From the outset, ask yourself what needs to happen for you to judge your project a success. Then ask what are the *important* issues that could go wrong and threaten that success. Systematic management of risk helps you decide:

- who should be made accountable for the actions to control the risk
- to whom it is commercially beneficial to transfer part of the cost of the risk
- when you need to make such decisions.

"There must be a beginning of any great matter, but the continuing unto the end until it be thoroughly finished yields the true glory."

Sir Francis Drake, 1587.

THE RISK MANAGER'S TOOL BOXES

Introduction

3 The risk management process

This section of the Guide provides a series of tools developed and used by practitioners of systematic risk management. If you decide to introduce risk management into your own organisation, start by reading Section 3 which describes the systematic process. In conjunction with that Section, Tool Boxes 1 and 2 give you step-by-step guidance on how to do your own first pass risk assessment and implement the system. Tool Boxes 3 and 4 offer you a window (but not in-depth guidance) on some of the more advanced, recognised techniques, so that you may appreciate the range of methods now available. You may wish to explore these with expert help at a later stage.

How to use the Tool Boxes

TOOLS FOR YOU AND YOUR ADVISERS

4 Who should do your risk assessment?

No set procedure can be appropriate to all clients. The Risk Manager is like a craftsman who applies his experience and tools to his objective or task. With use, you and your team can adapt the Tool Boxes to your needs. Bear in mind that:

- procedure is useful in protecting your business from inexperience and poor judgement, but *good* judgement is vital to risk management
- change is at the root of many risk issues; rigid procedure can be a reflection of past requirements which creates a sense of false security in the face of change
- most organisations have standard procedures, but few have mechanisms to adapt the procedure to the particular issue.

TOOLS FOR LEARNING

Risk management is a learning process, for example:

- continuous adding to a what can go wrong list helps avoid repeated mistakes
- a prompt list can fire useful risk identification debate (it is worth considering additions and deletions at the end of a session)
- all involved in the risk assessment process can be encouraged to send a copy of their concerns whenever they arise to the risk register file for consideration at the next review.

TOOL BOX 1   RISK IDENTIFICATION TECHNIQUES

**T 1.1 WHAT CAN
GO WRONG ANALYSIS**

 T1.3 Prompt lists

 3.6 Hazard and risk
identification

E.g. Using the project activity list to help
identify hazards

Lateral thinking is needed here. First decide your assessment objective. It may be a health and safety risk, or risk to cost, programme or quality, or risk to any other objective or aspect of the construction project, e.g. possible settlement in the floor leading to damage to your forklift trucks.

Start the identification process from a consideration of known hazards, e.g. fire, or address the risks as they stand. You need to identify what has the potential to harm your objective. If you have an activity plan, for example, you can consider what might go wrong in each action.

Activity 201:	Estimate cost of earthworks
What can go wrong:	Earthwork construction costs exceed tender sums
Detail:	Increase in sub-contractor rates increases cost of contractor claims. Works contractor has under-priced construction on several packages. Tender based on preliminary designs. Design changes probable. Underestimate of unsuitable fill material increases both imported and exported material. Fly tipping by haulage contractor.

**T 1.2 FREE AND
STRUCTURED
BRAINSTORMING**

 4.2 Use a facilitator

Free brainstorming involves recording what you think can go wrong. It can be done individually but works better with a group. In this case it is helpful to:

- appoint a facilitator whose role is to combine the function of chairman and helmsman
- record the process on a flip chart.

Free brainstorming can be a good warm-up exercise for structured brainstorming because it allows you and your team to identify quickly obvious concerns. The systematic process of risk management goes further by directing you towards more subtle or unusual topics. Brainstorming tends to be more effective if undertaken in short bursts of two hours or less. If more than five people participate, effectiveness is reduced.

Activity lists and works programmes are useful prompts. Work through the list to identify risks to the objective.

T 1.3 PROMPT LISTS

Prompt lists may be used to stimulate specific risk identification. An example list is provided below. Do not use checklists for this exercise, as they tend to identify the usual.

E.g. Design, construction and operation prompt list

Competence	Site investigation	Change
Ignorance	Settlement/Landslide	Non-completion
Fallibility	Leakage	Errors
Uncertainty	Flooding	Defects
Competition	Fire	Practicality
Communications	Explosion	Terrorism
Transport	Contamination	Vandalism
Team work	Pollution	Corruption
Forecasts	Archaeological	Programme
Assumptions	Services	Temporary works
Permissions	Performance	Cost
Instructions	Briefs	Legislation
Approvals	Security	Royalties
Long delivery	Availability	Patents
Regulations	Compatibility	Liabilities
Access	Reliability	Warranties
Confined spaces	Durability	Tax
Safety	Buildability	Blight
Toxicity	Repairability	Theft
Health	Workmanship	Labour relations
Accidents	Maintenance	Sub-contractors
Impact	Records	Public
Weather	Lifting	User
Earthquake	Dropping	Commissioning
Environment	Falling	Abandonment

Another form of prompt list is a "what can go wrong" list. An example of items that may be included on such a list is given below.

E.g. What can go wrong list

"What can go wrong" - example list

1.   Design brief/project objectives unclear
2.   Unproven design solutions adopted
3.   Problems with supply base, e.g. single source materials
4.   Interface/integration problem for equipment installation
5.   Known failure of technology not identified
6.   Unforeseen poor ground conditions encountered
7.   Industrial relations problems
8.   Adverse effects of legislation
9.   Inadequate project funding
10. Contract awarded on basis of lowest cost rather than quality.
11. Capability of contractor not matched to job
12. Lack of quality control
13. Inadequate project management
14. Poor team communications
15. Personality clashes within project team
16. Contractor goes bankrupt
17. Project subject to unnecessary constraints
18. Delays in obtaining planning permission

T 1.4 USE OF RECORDS

As you implement systematic methods, you begin to create valuable records which serve as an objective focus on your most salient risk issues. Check also through any existing records. This may help you determine more frequent causes of harm. For example, when assessing health and safety risk, it is useful to note the major causes of construction deaths based on records held by the Health and Safety Executive are:

People falling	52%
Falling materials/objects	19%
Transport/mobile plant	18%
Electrical hazards	5%
Asphyxiation/drowning	3%
Fire/explosion	2%
Other hazards	1%

However, take care when interpreting this type of data, as the fundamental cause of the harm may not be that attributed. For example, people falling may be due to lack of training, lack of equipment or other phenomena. It is also found that the above figures vary considerably when further analysed by trade, age, company size, etc.

T 1.5 STRUCTURED INTERVIEWS

If some of your concerns require specialist input, organise an interview with a qualified professional:

- prepare a set of open questions (i.e. questions that avoid anticipating an answer)
- send the questions in advance to the interviewee
- agree confidentiality and whether it is acceptable to use a tape recorder
- record the outcome in terms of the understanding you have gained and if necessary confirm it by sending the interviewee a copy inviting comment.

T 1.6 HINDSIGHT REVIEWS AND CASE EXAMPLES

Towards the end of a phase of work or project, it is often beneficial to the team members to meet to discuss what went wrong and how the project could have been better executed. You can avoid the problem of blame by using the process simply to update the prompt lists and add to the what can go wrong lists.

It is quite helpful to keep a note of how many times particular prompts are identified at the hindsight reviews. Frequent identification is indicative of an endemic risk which may warrant special attention.

The outcome of reviews can promote instinctive risk management and risk control culture within your organisation and those of your advisors and contractors.

You can use some of the more amusing case examples in staff bulletins or staff training, but if you do, keep them simple. Research shows that complex case examples are rejected as being "not relevant to my problem"; whereas people are receptive to single-issue anecdotes, parables and jokes that make a relevant point.

TOOL BOX 2   RISK REGISTERS AND RISK ASSESSMENT

T 2.1 PURPOSE OF REGISTER

The risk register is a means of recording and controlling the risk management process. Remember, however, that it is impossible to identify all risks and the register is no substitute for competence in decision-making.

T 2.2 CONTENTS OF REGISTER

In its simplest form the register will:

- describe the existing risk
- record possible risk reduction (mitigation) actions.

Depending on the circumstances, it can also provide:

- subdivision of risk into more detail
- a measure of likelihood (probability) and consequences
- identification of ownership of the risks
- importance/cost/acceptability of the risk
- practicality of mitigation action
- cost and ownership of action
- timing of action
- assessment of the residual risk
- change in importance/cost/acceptability of the risk as a result of mitigation action
- measure of cost benefit.

If you want to include all of this information in your register, devise a series of reports. The full register can be kept in a spreadsheet if desired. Examples of two forms of risk register are provided in Tables 2 and 3.

3.7 Risk assessment

Start your risk assessment bearing in mind *the current state of your project*. Construction practice usually includes some risk reduction measures and you need to take these into account. Backtracking to all the initial hazards may waste your time.

T 2.3 SOURCE OF RISK

Use the outcome of the risk identification exercise (Tool Box 1) to describe the risk in the register. This description should be both specific to the project and concise. Vague generalities may conceal an important issue.

T 2.4 RISK ASSESSMENT

Guidelines on measuring the likelihood and consequence of risk are given in Section 3 and Tables 4 and 5.

3.8 Likelihood of risk
3.9 Consequence of risk

You need only identify approximate values in multiples of ten, within a range that you consider relevant to your project (say, 1 to 10,000 years or £1,000 up to £10 million). If the range of outcomes appears to be too large to fit into a single box, consider redefining the risk under more than one heading by identifying the features that differentiate the risk. This will also help when identifying practical mitigation actions.

Three ways of assessing the risks are shown in Tables 6, 7 and 8. You can use:

- scale points to provide importance ranking (Table 6)
- monetary values to provide risk cost estimates (Table 7)
- qualitative descriptions to establish acceptability (Table 8).

Acceptable outcomes lie towards the lower right-hand corner of the tables. Outcomes on the top left are those requiring special attention.

T 2.5 REFLECTING BIAS IN TOLERATION OF RISK

You may wish to weight assessment values to reflect the severity of effect of a risk on your business. It may be that frequent marginal risks are more important than the occasional severe one. For example, travellers may be more tolerant of a two-hour delay every six months than of a ten-minute delay once a week. Alternatively, you may be more concerned about the infrequent catastrophic risks than the more frequent marginal risk. It is particularly important to consider such bias when evaluating safety issues.

T 2.6 ACCEPTABILITY OF RISK

When judging the acceptability of the risk, you may use the following as a starting point:

Description	Guidance
Unacceptable	Intolerable, must be eliminated or transferred
Undesirable	To be avoided if reasonably practicable, detailed investigation and cost benefit justification required, top level approval needed, monitoring essential
Acceptable	Can be accepted provided the risk is managed
Negligible	No further consideration needed.

T 2.7 USE OF QUESTIONNAIRES

You can use a proforma of the risk register as a questionnaire, provided that you add instructions and ensure you collect full details of the issues. A sample set of forms is provided as Tables 9, 10, 11 and 12. The questionnaire in Tables 10 and 12 focus on cost, programme and quality risks but with minor title changes can be modified to address other types of risk such as safety or environmental. The questionnaires may be used to gather information from members of your risk management team or others involved in the work if appropriate.

T 2.8 RISK MITIGATION AND RESIDUAL RISK

First list all the actions you could take to reduce or mitigate the risks you have identified. The emphasis here is on practical possibilities. The mitigating action may eliminate the risk altogether or just reduce it.

3.10 Risk mitigation

One way of assessing the effectiveness of the mitigating action is to describe in simple terms how much risk is left (residual risk). The residual risk may depend on factors outside your control and a description of it may be quite helpful, if only as a reminder. You may dismiss some risks as unimportant and probe others which look particularly threatening. A rough cost estimate of risk mitigation measures helps clarify priorities. However, risk assessment is not based on cost alone. If you take steps to control or eliminate risks, record your actions in the risk register and assess your residual risks.

T 2.9 WHEN TO STOP THE ASSESSMENT

Assembling your first risk register can yield substantial cost benefits, particularly when it is undertaken at an early stage in the project. The process is subject to a law of diminishing returns, however, as the risk management plans are implemented. It is worth noting that further work can be of particular benefit:

- when management is not sufficiently convinced to approve the necessary action
- when the team undertaking the assessment is lacking in an element of experience or knowledge
- when the risk arises from a combination of events
- when the risk arises from interaction of a number of different parties or disciplines (e.g. designer, contractor, lawyer, financier)
- when the risk arises from change, novelty, or serious lack of data or information
- when the risk arises from or depends on human attitudes.

In each case a better understanding or a clearer presentation of the issues is needed.

Take care not to prolong assessment unduly, or it may hold up the progress of the work. This phenomenon is often called "paralysis by analysis".

Review the risk register at about six month intervals or prior to any major decisions or changes to the project e.g. land acquisition, issue and award of tenders.

E.g. How to use the Risk Register

Table 3 is an extract from a Risk Register to assess risk arising from an earthworks sub-contract on a supermarket construction project. Three ways of assessing risk are presented.

Scale points for importance ranking

Risks may be assessed and ranked on a simple scale points basis.

Fly tipping is assessed as being likely to occur many times during the contract. Referring to Table 4, the likelihood is classified as "frequent" with a score of 4.

It is believed the cost of each fly tipping incident can be absorbed within the contract contingency. Referring to Table 5, the consequence is assessed as "marginal" with a score of 1.

The impact of the risk is assessed by multiplying the likelihood score 4 by the consequence score 1 to give a risk importance ranking score of 4 (see Table 6).

To mitigate the risk, a specific requirement will be included in the main contract to ensure only approved tips and haulage contractors are used. This is assessed as reducing the likelihood of fly tipping to "remote" with a score of 1, in turn reducing the importance ranking score to 1.

Risk cost estimates

Risks may be evaluated on a monetary basis using estimates of risk cost.

Firstly, the nominal values of the scales for likelihood and consequence in Tables 4 and 5 need to be set.

For this example, the period of concern is taken to be one year as this is the duration of the earthworks contract. Hence, T in Table 4 is taken as 1 year and the unit of time on which the probability values are based becomes years. A "serious" consequence is assessed to be £10k, this being equal to the contingency sum for the sub-contract. Hence, V in Table 5 is taken as £10k.

Table 7 may be used to estimate the risk cost. The likelihood of fly tipping incidents is assessed as 100 times per year with the cost of each incident estimated at £1k, including for hidden costs such as adverse publicity. Hence the risk cost is assessed as 100x£1k=£100k per year. The mitigation action is considered to reduce the likelihood of fly tipping to once in ten years, i.e. 0.1 times per year. The consequence of each incident is however unchanged by the mitigation action. Hence, the cost of the residual risk if the mitigation action is adopted is estimated at 0.1x£1k=£100 per year.

When evaluating the benefit of the mitigation action, account must be taken of secondary risks, which in this case could be an increase in tender costs to accommodate the extra contract conditions.

Risk acceptability

The arguments for determining likelihood and consequence are the same as for the importance ranking method described above. Risks are assessed qualitatively using the descriptions for risk acceptability given in a Section T2.6 together with Table 8.

Table 2   Project risk register - risk identification

PROJECT - RISK REGISTER RISK IDENTIFICATION

Date / Revision   Authorship / Approval

No	Risk description	Detail	Elimination - Mitigation — Action	Residual Risk
1	Earthwork construction costs exceed tender sums.	Fly tipping by haulage contractor causes adverse publicity with possible knock-on clean-up costs.	Include contractual requirement for only approved tips and approved haulage contractors to be used.	Risk is reduced to acceptable level but not eliminated.
		Tenders based on preliminary designs. Design changes likely.	Accelerate structure designs and freeze volumes prior to start of earthworks. Implement efficient change control. Include suitable contract variation provisions.	Effectiveness of mitigation will depend on design teams ability to understand owner's requirements and owners determination to control costs in spite of possible compromise on space available.

See Tables 9 to 12 for questionnaire

Table 3   Project risk register - risk assessment

PROJECT - RISK REGISTER RISK ASSESSMENT

Date / Revision   Authorship / Approval

No	Risk description — Detail	Assessment — Owner	Likely	Conseq	Assess	Mitigation action	Likely	Conseq	Assess	When	Who
1	Fly tipping by haulage contractor causes adverse publicity with possible knock-on clean-up costs.	Client	4 / 100/y / Freq	1 / £1k / Marg	4 / £100k/y / Undes	Include contract requirement for only approved tips and haulage contractors to be used.	1 / 0.1/y / Rem	1 / £1k / Marg	1 / £100/y / Accept	Tender	PM
	Tenders based on preliminary designs. Design changes likely.	Client	3 / 10/y / Prob	2 / £10k / Ser	6 / £100k/y / Undes	a) Accelerate structure designs and freeze prior to start of earthworks. b) Include suitable contract variation provisions. c) Implement efficient change control.	2 / 1/y / Occ	1 / £1k / Marg	2 / £1k/y / Accept	a) Design, prior to award. b) Tender c) Construction	a) Des b) PM c) PM

KEY: PM = Project Manager, Des = Designer

See Tables 4 to 8 and E.g. How to use the Risk Register for assessment guidance

Table 4   Typical scales for likelihood/probability

LIKELIHOOD / PROBABILITY			
Description	**Guidance**	**Scale**	**Probability***
Frequent	Likely to occur frequently, many times during the period of concern (e.g. project duration, life of the building).	4	100/T
Probable	Several times in the period of concern.	3	10/T
Occasional	Some time in the period of concern.	2	1/T
Remote	Unlikely but possible in the period of concern (e.g. once in ten times the life of the building).	1	1/10T
Improbable	So unlikely that it can be assumed that it will not occur or it cannot occur.	0	1/100T
* See Section 3.8 for help when deciding a nominal value of time T.			

Table 5   Typical scales for consequence

CONSEQUENCE			
Description	**Guidance**	**Scale**	**Cost***
Catastrophic	Death, system loss, criminal guilt, bankruptcy.	4	£100V
Critical	Occupation threatening injury or illness, major damage, substantial damages, exceeds contingency, dividend at risk.	3	£10V
Serious	Lost time injury or illness, damage causing down time of plant, consumes contingency, requires an insurance claim.	2	£V
Marginal	Injury or illness requiring first aid at work only, minor damage that can await routine maintenance, will only require an apology letter, accommodated as part of contingency or insurance excess.	1	£V/10
Negligible	So minor as to be regarded as without consequence.	0	£V/100
* See Section 3.9 for help when deciding a nominal value of cost £V.			

Table 6 Assessment of risk importance

RISK IMPORTANCE

LIKELIHOOD SCALE	CONSEQUENCE SCALE	Catastrophic 4	Critical 3	Serious 2	Marginal 1	Negligible 0
Frequent	4	16	12	8	4	0
Probable	3	12	9	6	3	0
Occasional	2	8	6	4	2	0
Remote	1	4	3	2	1	0
Improbable	0	0	0	0	0	0

Table 7 Assessment of risk cost

RISK COST £ / UNIT TIME

LIKELIHOOD PROBABILITY	CONSEQUENCE COST	Catastrophic £100V	Critical £10V	Serious £V	Marginal $\frac{£V}{10}$	Negligible $\frac{£V}{100}$
Frequent	100/T	10000V/T	1000V/T	100V/T	10V/T	V/T
Probable	10/T	1000V/T	100V/T	10V/T	V/T	V/10T
Occasional	1/T	100V/T	10V/T	V/T	V/10T	V/100T
Remote	1/10T	10V/T	V/T	V/10T	V/100T	V/1000T
Improbable	1/100T	V/T	V/10T	V/100T	V/1000T	V/10000T

See Sections 3.8 and 3.9 for help when deciding nominal values for time T and cost £V.

Table 8 Assessment of risk acceptability

RISK ACCEPTABILITY

LIKELIHOOD \ CONSEQUENCE	Catastrophic	Critical	Serious	Marginal	Negligible
Frequent	Unacceptable	Unacceptable	Unacceptable	Undesirable	Undesirable
Probable	Unacceptable	Unacceptable	Undesirable	Undesirable	Acceptable
Occasional	Unacceptable	Undesirable	Undesirable	Acceptable	Acceptable
Remote	Undesirable	Undesirable	Acceptable	Acceptable	Negligible
Improbable	Undesirable	Acceptable	Acceptable	Negligible	Negligible

Key:	Description	Guidance
	Unacceptable	Intolerable, must be eliminated or transferred
	Undesirable	To be avoided if reasonably practicable, detailed investigation and cost benefit justification required, top level approval needed, monitoring essential
	Acceptable	Can be accepted provided the risk is managed
	Negligible	No further consideration needed.

Table 9   Typical risk identification
questionnaire

RISK QUESTIONNAIRE		
PROJECT: *Name of project*	Form author:	Page no: Date: Revision:
Purpose of form: DESCRIPTION OF CURRENT RISK		Return to:
ASSESSMENT OBJECTIVE: *Risk to budget, programme, quality, safety, environment, etc.*		
RISK DESCRIPTION: *A short description to label the risk*		
ACTIVITY DESCRIPTION: *Description of the activity from which the risk stems*		
DETAILED DESCRIPTION OF THE RISK: *Description of its source, the way the risk materialises and its primary consequences*		
DESCRIPTION OF SUBSEQUENT OR KNOCK-ON EFFECTS: *Description of knock-on effects and linkage to other activities where their consequences could be escalated*		
CURRENT OWNERSHIP: Who is damaged? Who will pay? Who is able to manage the risk?		

Table 10 Typical risk assessment
questionnaire

RISK QUESTIONNAIRE						

RISK QUESTIONNAIRE

PROJECT: *Name of project*	Form author:	Page no: Date: Revision:

Purpose of form: TO ASSESS LIKELIHOOD, CONSEQUENCE AND IMPORTANCE OF CURRENT RISK	Return to:

RISK DESCRIPTION:

Short description from Table 9

SCALE POINTS: *see Tables 4 and 5*	0	1	2	3	4
LIKELIHOOD:					

Reasons for selection of box

CONSEQUENCE: IMPACT ON PROGRAMME:					

Reasons for selection of box

CONSEQUENCE: IMPACT ON COSTS:					

Reasons for selection of box

CONSEQUENCE: IMPACT ON QUALITY:					

Reasons for selection of box

IMPORTANCE (assessor to complete):	Programme					
	Costs					
	Quality					
	Overall					

Table 11 Typical risk mitigation identification questionnaire

RISK QUESTIONNAIRE		
PROJECT: *Name of project*	Form author:	Page no: Date: Revision:
Purpose of form: DESCRIPTION OF POSSIBLE MITIGATION		Return to:
RISK DESCRIPTION: *Short description from Table 9*		
DESCRIPTION OF POSSIBLE RISK REDUCTION MEASURES: *Description of measures that will reduce or eliminate the risk*		
DESCRIPTION OF SECONDARY RISKS: *Description of new risks that could arise from the reduction measures described*		
DESCRIPTION OF RESIDUAL RISKS: *Description of risks that will still exist after the measures have been implemented*		
OWNERSHIP: *Identify who owns the residual risk*		
ACTION PLAN: *Description of actions needed to implement risk reduction described*	BY WHOM: *Who implements the actions*	WHEN: *Identify when action can or must be taken*
ESTIMATED COST OF ACTION:		

Table 12 Typical residual risk
assessment questionnaire

RISK QUESTIONNAIRE							
PROJECT: *Name of project*		Form author:		Page no: Date: Revision:			
Purpose of form: TO ASSESS RESIDUAL RISK AFTER MITIGATION ACTIONS IMPLEMENTED				Return to:			
RISK DESCRIPTION: *Short description from Table 9*							
SCALE POINTS: *see Tables 4 and 5*			0	1	2	3	4
LIKELIHOOD: *Reasons for selection of box*							
CONSEQUENCE: IMPACT ON PROGRAMME: *Reasons for selection of box*							
CONSEQUENCE: IMPACT ON COSTS: *Reasons for selection of box*							
CONSEQUENCE: IMPACT ON QUALITY: *Reasons for selection of box*							
IMPORTANCE (assessor to complete):	Programme						
	Costs						
	Quality						
	Overall						

TOOL BOX 3   SYSTEMATIC CAPTURE OF THE PROBLEM

T 3.1 THE LOGIC OF RISKS

Risks are often the result of a series of logically connected and probably familiar events or actions which combine to cause the damage. Usually, therefore, you can assess a risk more easily if you have identified the logic behind its components. Capturing the problem in this way helps you decide where to focus your effort in reducing the risk. Some methods of systematic capture are introduced here and in Tool Box 4.

T 3.2 DECISION TREES

Start by relating a decision to its possible outcomes:

- set down the possible outcomes of the decision
- set down the options open to you
- identify the possible outcomes of each option
- attach estimates of cost to each option
- if you feel uncertain, estimate the odds for each outcome
- multiply the costs by the odds and compare the results.

E.g. Decision tree - selection of design/ construct approach

You need to decide whether to use a traditional "design then build" approach or employ a "design and build" contractor. You have estimated that there is a 10% chance that the design will have to be changed after the award of the design and build contract, in which case costs will increase by £50,000 to accommodate the reconstruction and acceleration required to meet the programme.

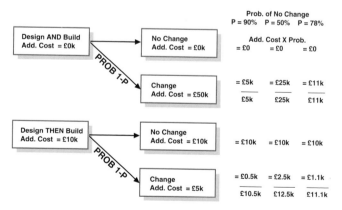

The design then build approach is estimated to cost £10,000 more initially to offset the longer programme to completion. The cost of accommodating the change is estimated to be £5,000 for abortive design work if design then build is adopted. The 90% probability of no change implies a 10% probability that the change will be required, in which case it appears better to adopt the design and build approach, provided you can afford the £50k cost escalation if it happens. If the probability of a change is 50% then there are clear savings from the design then build approach. The break-even is a probability of change of about 22%.

If you are not confident in the estimates, try the following:

- consider how much the odds (or cost estimate) have to be adjusted to get an equal cost for each option
- ask yourself if you could be so far out in your estimate.

T 3.3 FAULT TREES

A fault tree is a method of representing the logical combinations of various states which lead to a particular outcome, known as the top event. An example of a top event is a fire inside a lift shaft.

Prepare the fault tree by working backwards from the resultant adverse event to:

- identify the conditions required for the top event to occur
- identify the sub-conditions required for each condition, continuing the process until the root causes are identified

E.g. Fault tree for fire in a lift shaft

An example of a simple fault tree is given below. You wish to consider the risk of a fire in a lift shaft. Begin at the bottom branch of the tree. (NB: The "bottom" of the tree corresponds to the top box in the diagram below.) For a fire to occur, a source of fuel and ignition and oxygen need to be simultaneously present. Assume that oxygen is always present. Fuel and ignition can be either "built in" or "brought in". The "built in" sources of fuel and ignition are identified as "grease" or "equipment" respectively or "etc" (indicating that you may not have thought of all sources) and so on.

Although not shown here, by adding estimated likelihoods of each of the root causes, you can use the fault tree to review the means of eliminating or controlling the sources of risk.

The fault tree allows:

- development of an understanding of the problem
- highlighting of inherent risks
- review of the permutations of sub-events which could lead to the top event
- calculation of the overall likelihood of the top event or any sub-conditions
- management of the problem, focusing on its root causes.

T 3.4 EVENT TREES

Event trees illustrate the intermediate and final outcomes which may arise after an initial event. An example is the assessment of the knock-on effects of your main contractor going bankrupt. Some of the consequences of his bankruptcy may affect cost and programme; others may not.

E.g. Event tree for the contractor going bankrupt

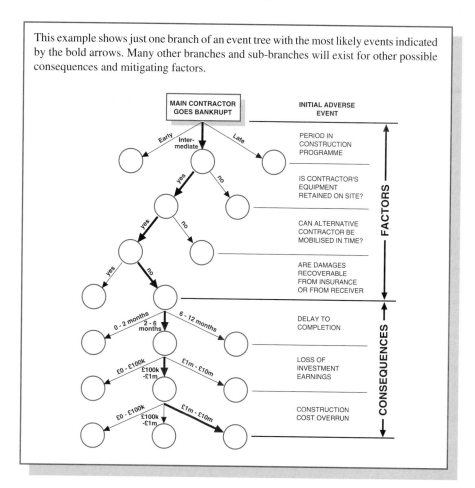

This example shows just one branch of an event tree with the most likely events indicated by the bold arrows. Many other branches and sub-branches will exist for other possible consequences and mitigating factors.

You can prepare event trees in a similar way to fault trees except that you work forwards from your initial adverse event to establish the range of consequences. The likelihood of each consequence needs to be estimated.

The event tree allows you to:

- establish the scope of the consequences of an adverse event with mitigating factors
- review the seriousness of each consequence in the context of all consequences
- estimate the overall likelihood of any consequence or set of consequences
- review options for the management of the potential consequences in context of the conditions which gave rise to them.

T3.5 SENSITIVITY ANALYSIS

To compare the magnitude of individual uncertainties and identify where to focus your risk reduction effort, it is well worth plotting (or just sketching) a sensitivity ("spider") diagram. This highlights the most serious risks and their effects on the whole project.

E.g. Sensitivity analysis

You are considering the viability of building a new factory. You have identified a number of key variables that you believe are potentially serious for the outturn of your project. Plotting the effect of changes in these variables on the change in the internal rate of return for your project reveals that revenue from your product and timely completion of construction are your most sensitive risks. Consequently you may wish to adjust your project strategy by commissioning further market surveys to increase confidence in your sales forecasts, or make sure that during construction your efforts are focused on keeping the project on programme at the expense of additional costs.

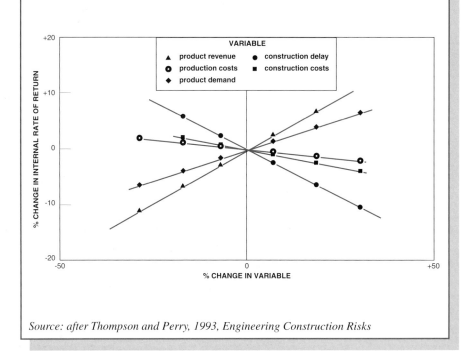

Source: after Thompson and Perry, 1993, Engineering Construction Risks

Such an assessment has limitations in that risks are considered independently and without consideration of probability of occurrence. However, the technique is simple and helps you predict the relative sensitivity of the outturn of the project to variations in assumed values of key risk factors.

T 3.6 COST CONTINGENCY ANALYSIS

5.10 Contingency management

T4.2 Improving estimates

The cost plan for a project is based on estimates which are prey to many uncertainties such as inflation and prediction of quantities. You can use traditional tools such as spreadsheets to create cost models and produce budget estimates, allowing for assumed contingencies. However, some cost estimates may be subject to great uncertainty. If so, you can use risk modelling techniques to assign probability distributions to the estimated values. There are various extensions to spreadsheets available to undertake such analysis. The method is known as *Monte Carlo* simulation. The computer selects a value from each of the distributions "at random" and repeats the analysis several hundred times to provide a probability distribution for the total estimate. This provides a basis for assigning contingency.

It is better to assign costs to the basic activities so that duration dependent elements can be included in the calculation.

The basic steps are as follows:

- summarise the programme into about 30 - 50 activities
- assemble the cost estimate on a spreadsheet with risk modelling capability
- assign parameters to the cost items that describe simplified probability distributions, for example, mean, upper and lower bound costs
- run the risk model to produce the probability distribution of cost
- extract best estimates, sometimes called 50/50 (i.e. 50% chance of being exceeded) and other confidence levels as desired
- decide contingency values based on the importance you attach to avoiding an overrun.

Base your selection of activities on the nature of the uncertainty. The cost of some items can be connected. If the quantity of concrete is increased, so is that of the shuttering. Some items such as hire of scaffolding and site management will be dependent on programme duration. Include these in the same activity so that the same value is assigned to them. Without such care, the outcome can be seriously misleading.

Where one item dominates the cost estimate, it may be possible to break down the estimate to reflect uncertainty in physical parameters. The volume of fill and its cost could in part depend on the strength of the soil. The softer it is, the more that has to be replaced. Sub-models can be used to reflect such issues.

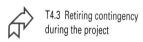
T4.3 Retiring contingency during the project

Allocate the contingency to activities on a rational basis, reflecting the level of uncertainty. As the activities are completed, reduce the contingency. In principle you can apply this method to any estimate where the value is made up of logically related components.

T 3.7 PROGRAMME RISK ANALYSIS

The timing of activities during construction depends on completion of earlier activities. For example, a wall cannot normally be built until its foundations are in place. The activities that determine the minimum time in which a project can be completed are said to be on the *critical path.*

Thus a delay in the delivery of the bricks will only delay the programme if delivery of bricks is on the critical path or moves onto the critical path owing to change in the timing of other activities.

These interactions are so important to the progress of construction work that in many cases the logic of the programme is captured in the form of a critical path network. Normally best estimate values are assigned to the activities and the logic is analysed to identify a critical path and an estimate of the completion date. With experience you can interpret this type of "one shot at a time" analysis to provide an intuitive feel for the reliability of the programme. You can analyse again to examine sensitivities to particular events, or to reflect partial completion of the work.

Your estimates of time needed to complete each activity are subject to uncertainty and you can undertake a *Monte Carlo* analysis to produce probability distributions for these estimates similar to that described in Section T 3.6.

The relationship of cost and time is changed if you accelerate progress. For example, your contractor may speed up work by authorising overtime or you may elect to provide temporary weatherproofing to allow work to proceed in the event of adverse weather. You can treat risk mitigation measures as programme activities and add them to the activity lists used for both cost and time analysis. Risk models of this type may also be used to identify the probability that particular activities may be on the critical path.

TOOL BOX 4   METHODS OF PRESENTATION OF RISK ANALYSIS RESULTS

T 4.1 WHAT DO THE RESULTS MEAN?

In risk analysis, you make key decisions based on perception of the uncertainties. You can use standard methods such as bar charts, histograms and cost comparisons to present the outcome of risk assessments and analyses simply and clearly. However, many more advanced methods exist for presentation of risk analysis results. An introduction to some of these methods is provided below.

T 4.2 IMPROVING ESTIMATES

You can present the uncertainty of estimates in an objective form, as described below.

E.g. Estimates for contingency

 2.8 Realistic estimates

 T3.6 Cost contingency analysis

The base estimate for a cost plan is assembled from estimates of each item. Contingencies are then added to reflect common types of risk, including interest or inflation rate fluctuations during the project. Experience or company policy may dictate a global contingency allowance for other risks. Research indicates that this type of contingency is normally used and sometimes overruns occur. This approach works where the risks are relatively small and not subject to changes. Your risk register demonstrates that the cost of items is uncertain. The degree of cost uncertainty depends on the nature of the risk inherent in that item. Some items such as foundations, weather dependent trades and special pieces of equipment are much more uncertain than, for example, off-the-shelf components. A more detailed estimate of contingency can be provided, but it does not measure the confidence that should be placed in the estimate. The diagram below shows a base estimate, with a probability distribution superimposed; it is generated using the methods described in Tool Box 3. This diagram can be used to identify the cost estimate which has only a 5% chance of being exceeded. This is called the 95% confidence limit. It is a way of specifying the contingency required to be reasonably sure that the project will be completed within budget.

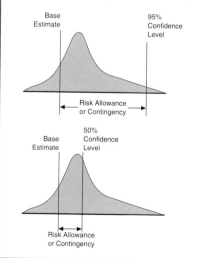

Normally the cost will end up near the centre of the distribution.

You can expect the project to have an equal chance of finishing above or below the 50% confidence level in the second plot.

If your company is large with a high number of small projects, you can afford to set your contingency at the 50% level, thereby releasing capital for other ventures.

Developing this type of contingency estimating method which reflects specific cost uncertainty can help decision-making.

T 4.3 RETIRING CONTINGENCY DURING THE PROJECT

As a project progresses, cost assumptions become facts and cost uncertainty therefore reduces. Contingency can be retired progressively giving you better control of the project by preventing surpluses being used later to cover up mismanagement. The uncertainty in cost estimates can be illustrated on what is known as a "torpedo model". The latter also shows the wisdom of developing a project to an advanced stage of design before committing major capital expenditure to it.

E.g. Torpedo model of cost uncertainty

5.10 Contingency management

The plot shows a typical torpedo model. It focuses on the probability distributions at the end of the feasibility study, on issue of tender documents and at settlement. The uncertainty is illustrated by the width of the distribution. The most likely values are marked M. The uncertainty is assumed to be limited by the 95% probability lines marked H (high limit) and L (low limit).

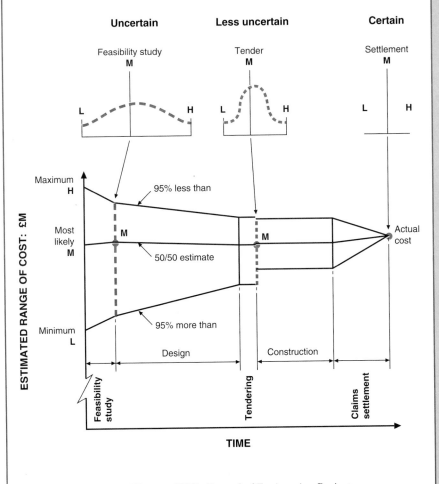

Source: after Barnes (in Wearne, 1989) Control of Engineering Projects

T 4.4 DECISION CONSEQUENCE MODEL

You can plot the probability of achieving an objective against a variable within your control to show how changing the variable increases your chances of success. The presentation can be extended to illustrate the effect of more variables by including several plots on one graph.

E.g. Decision consequence model

5.5 Risk management in the project programme

The Queen has agreed to open your new marina but the date has to be fixed prior to start of construction three years in advance. Construction of the main breakwaters and the installation of the floating hotel are weather dependent. You are able to vary the start date within a range of four months, but you want to keep the construction programme as short as possible to reduce cash flow costs. You also want to establish the opening date as early as possible in the sailing season so as to increase first year earnings. The results of a programme risk analysis are presented graphically below. The effect of varying the start date is obtained by sliding a vertical ruler along the horizontal axis and reading off the crossing points for each of the start dates. For example, a February 1st opening date has an 85% probability of being met if construction starts in September, but only 23% if the start is delayed until December.

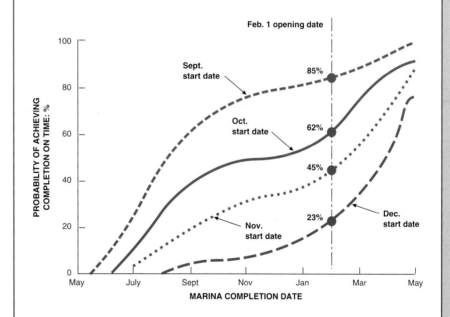

Source: after Thompson and Perry, 1993, Engineering Construction Risks

T 4.5 COST AND TIME PLOT

Sometimes your greatest business risk may be the need to adhere to a programme, for example, when you want to launch a product ahead of the competition. In other cases, minimum cost could be the main issue. As often as not, you need to strike a balance. The time cost plot below illustrates how the outcome of advanced risk analysis can provide you with an understanding of the relationship between the two.

The simple and easily interpreted plot that this type of assessment can produce hides the considerable modelling skill and effort required to simulate the effect properly.

E.g. Cost and time uncertainty model

5.5 Risk management in the project programme

A project assessment model has been run many times. The cost and completion date have been plotted for each outturn as a dot. The dots tend to cluster around the most likely outturn and become more sparse away from this area.

The plot serves to illustrate the cost estimate you can expect if you need a high level of certainty on a programme, or the programme you need to set if you wish to minimise cost or accommodate cost uncertainty.

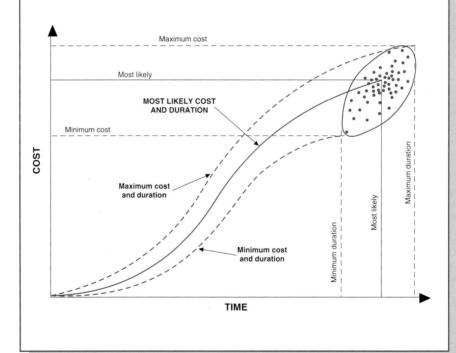

BIBLIOGRAPHY

Some of the more prominent texts available on the assessment and management of risk issues are assembled in this bibliography, together with other useful references including relevant legal documents, standards and health and safety publications.

Companion CIRIA Guides

Connaughton, J.N.
VALUE BY COMPETITION: A GUIDE TO THE COMPETITIVE PROCUREMENT OF CONSULTANCY SERVICES FOR CONSTRUCTION SP117
CIRIA, London, 1994

Potter, M.
PLANNING TO BUILD? A PRACTICAL INTRODUCTION TO THE CONSTRUCTION PROCESS SP113
CIRIA, London, 1995

Connaughton, J.N. and Green, S.D.
VALUE MANAGEMENT IN UK PRACTICE
CIRIA, London (to be published 1996)

Other introductory guidance on the analysis and management of construction risk

The Engineering Council
CODE OF PROFESSIONAL PRACTICE: ENGINEERS AND RISK ISSUES
Engineering Council, London, 1992

HM Treasury, Central Unit on Procurement
GUIDANCE NO 41 MANAGING RISK AND CONTINGENCY FOR WORKS PROJECTS
HMSO, London, 1993

Thompson, P.A. and Perry, J.G.
ENGINEERING CONSTRUCTION RISKS: A GUIDE TO PROJECT RISK ANALYSIS AND RISK MANAGEMENT
Thomas Telford, London, 1993

The Engineering Council
GUIDELINES ON RISK ISSUES
Engineering Council, London, 1993

Norris, C., Perry, J.G. and Simon, P.
PROJECT RISK ANALYSIS AND MANAGEMENT, A GUIDE BY THE ASSOCIATION OF PROJECT MANAGERS
CPS Project Management Ltd, Aberdeen, 1992

Other useful books and guidance

British Safety Council
EMERGENCY PLANNING AND DISASTER CONTROL - MANAGEMENT SELF-AUDIT
British Safety Council, London

Cooper, D.F. and Chapman, C.B.
RISK ANALYSIS FOR LARGE PROJECTS
Wiley, London, 1987

Chartered Insurance Institute
650 CONSTRUCTION INSURANCE
CII, London, 1991 (supplementary notes 1994)

Cox, S.J. and Tait, N.R.
RELIABILITY, SAFETY AND RISK MANAGEMENT
Butterworth/Heinemann, London, 1991

European Construction Institute
TOTAL PROJECT MANAGEMENT OF
CONSTRUCTION SAFETY,
HEALTH AND ENVIRONMENT
Thomas Telford, London, 1992

HM Treasury, Central Unit on Purchasing
GUIDANCE NO 36 CONTRACT STRATEGY
SELECTION FOR MAJOR PROJECTS
London, 1992

Kleiz, T.A.
AN ENGINEER'S VIEW OF HUMAN
ERROR
The Institution of Chemical Engineers,
London, 1991

Loss Prevention Council
LPC CODE OF PRACTICE FOR THE
CONSTRUCTION OF BULDINGS
LPC, London, 1992

Royal Society
RISK: ANALYSIS, PERCEPTION AND
MANAGEMENT
The Royal Society, London, 1992

Toft, B. and Reynolds, S.A.
LEARNING FROM DISASTERS: A
MANAGEMENT APPROACH
Butterworth/Heinemann, London, 1994

Wearne, S.H. (Ed)
CONTROL OF ENGINEERING PROJECTS
Thomas Telford, London, 1989

World Bank
WORKSHOP ON SAFETY CONTROL AND
RISK MANAGEMENT
Karlstad, Sweden, November 1989.

Flanagan, R. and Norman, G.
RISK MANAGEMENT AND
CONSTRUCTION
Blackwell, Oxford, 1993

Kleiz, T.A.
HAZOP AND HAZAN: NOTES ON THE
IDENTIFICATION AND ASSESSMENT OF
HAZARDS
The Institution of Chemical Engineers,
London, 1992

Latham, M.
CONSTRUCTING THE TEAM
Final report of the government / industry
review of procurement and contractual
arrangements in the construction industry
HMSO, London, 1994

McGowan, P.H., Malcolm, R., Horner, W.,
Jones, D. and Thompson, P.A.
ALLOCATION AND EVALUATION OF
RISK IN CONSTRUCTION CONTRACTS
CIOB, Ascot, 1992

Safety and Reliability Society
ENGINEERS AND RISK ISSUES
Proceedings of the symposium held at
Altrincham edited by C.F. Cox and I.A.Watson.
SARS Ltd., Manchester, 1993

US Department of Defence
MILITARY STANDARD, SAFETY SYSTEM
PROGRAMME REQUIREMENTS
MIL-STD-882C, USGPO, Washington, 1993

Webb, A
MANAGING INNOVATIVE PROJECTS
Chapman Hall, London, 1994

Relevant health and safety publications

Confederation of British Industry
DEVELOPING A SAFETY CULTURE:
BUSINESS FOR SAFETY
CBI, London, 1990

CIRIA
A GUIDE TO THE CONTROL OF
SUBSTANCES HAZARDOUS TO HEALTH
IN DESIGN AND CONSTRUCTION,
Report R125
CIRIA with Thomas Telford, London, 1993

CIRIA
CDM REGULATIONS - CASE STUDY
GUIDANCE FOR DESIGNERS: AN
INTERIM REPORT, Report R145
CIRIA, London, 1995

Health and Safety Commission
HUMAN RELIABILITY ASSESSMENT -
A CRITICAL OVERVIEW
Second report of advisory committee on the
safety of nuclear installations study group on
human factors.
HSE Books, Sudbury, 1991

Health and Safety Executive
A GUIDE TO MANAGING HEALTH AND
SAFETY IN CONSTRUCTION
HSE Books, Sudbury, 1995

Health and Safety Executive
DESIGNING FOR HEALTH AND SAFETY
IN CONSTRUCTION
A guide for designers on the Construction
(Design and Management) Regulations 1994
HSE Books, Sudbury, 1995

Health and Safety Executive
HS(G) 48 HUMAN FACTORS IN
INDUSTRIAL SAFETY,
HSE Books, Sudbury, 1989

Health and Safety Executive
MANAGING CONSTRUCTION FOR
HEALTH AND SAFETY; CONSTRUCTION
(DESIGN AND MANAGEMENT)
REGULATIONS 1994 APPROVED CODE OF
PRACTICE
HSE Books, Sudbury, 1995

Health and Safety Executive
QUANTIFIED RISK ASSESSMENT: ITS
INPUT TO DECISION MAKING
HSE Books, Sudbury, 1989

Health and Safety Executive
THE COST OF ACCIDENTS AT WORK
HSE Books, Sudbury, 1993

Health and Safety Executive
CDM REGULATIONS; HOW THE
REGULATIONS AFFECT YOU! PML54
HSE Books, Sudbury, 1995

Health and Safety Executive
HS(R)23 A GUIDE TO THE REPORTING OF
INJURIES, DISEASES AND DANGEROUS
OCCURRENCES REGULATIONS
HSE Books, Sudbury, 1985

Health and Safety Executive
IND(G)113 YOUR FIRM'S INJURY
RECORDS AND HOW TO USE THEM
HSE Books, Sudbury, 1991

Health and Safety Executive
MAJOR HAZARD ASSESSMENT: A
SURVEY OF CURRENT METHODOLOGY
AND INFORMATION SOURCES
Specialist Inspector Report (SIR) 29
HSE Books, Sudbury, 1991

Health and Safety Executive
RISK CRITERIA FOR LAND-USE
PLANNING IN THE VICINITY OF MAJOR
INDUSTRIAL HAZARDS
HSE Books, Sudbury, 1989

Health and Safety Executive
THE TOLERABILITY OF RISK FROM
NUCLEAR POWER STATIONS
HSE Books, Sudbury, 1992

Useful papers and proceedings on risk issues

Capper, P.
OVERVIEW OF RISK ON CONSTRUCTION
Proceedings from the seventh annual
conference of the centre of construction law
and management, Kings College (London),
Paper 1, London, 1994

Godfrey, P.S.
THE HOLISTIC APPROACH; COPING WITH
COMPLEXITY IN PROCUREMENT.
The Institution of Mechanical Engineers,
Railway Division, London, 1993

Hambly, E.C. and Hambly, E.A.
RISK EVALUATION AND REALISM
Proceedings of the Institution of Civil
Engineers, Civil Engineering, 102 (2), 1994,
p64-71

Rimington, J.D.
COPING WITH TECHNOLOGICAL RISK: A
21ST CENTURY PROBLEM
Royal Academy of Engineering, London, 1993

Capper, P.
PRACTICAL MANAGEMENT OF LEGAL
RISK
Royal Academy of Engineering, London, 1993

Godfrey, P.S.
CONTROL OF RISK
Proceedings from the seventh annual
conference of the centre of construction law
and management, Kings College (London),
Paper 2, London, 1994

Thompson, P.A. and Norris, C.
THE PERCEPTION, ANALYSIS AND
MANAGEMENT OF FINANCIAL RISK IN
ENGINEERING PROJECTS
Proceedings of the Institution of Civil
Engineers, Civil Engineering, 93 (1), 1993,
p42-47

Legal references

Note that there are a large number of supporting regulations in addition to the ones listed below.

Acts and Statutory Instruments:

Construction (Design and Management)
Regulations 1994
SI 1994/3140
HMSO, London, ISBN011043845

Consumer Protection Act 1987
HMSO, London, ISBN 0105443875

Control of Industrial Major Accident Hazards
Regulations 1984 (CIMAH) SI 1984/1902
HMSO, London, ISBN 0110479025

Control of Substances Hazardous to Health
Regulations 1994 (COSHH) SI 1994/3246
HMSO, London, ISBN 0110437217

Electricity at Work Regulations 1989
SI 1989/635
HMSO, London, ISBN 011096635X

Environmental Protection Act 1990
HMSO, London, ISBN 0105443905

Health and Safety at Work Act 1974
HMSO, London, ISBN 0105437743

Management of Health and Safety at Work
Regulations 1992 SI 1992/2051
HMSO, London, ISBN 0110250516

Management of Health and Safety at Work
(Amendment) Regulations 1994 SI 1994/2865
HMSO, London, ISBN 0110430212

Sale of Goods Act 1979
HMSO, London, ISBN 0105454796

Unfair Contract Terms Act 1977
HMSO, London, ISBN 0105450774

Other Acts and Directives:

European Commission Directive on the major
accident hazards of certain industrial activities
82/501/EEC Official Journal (L230), 1982

European Commission Directive on the
introduction of measures to encourage
improvements in the health and safety of works
at work 89/391/EEC Official Journal (L183/1),
1989

OECD Council Act
Decision recommendation concerning
provision of information to the public and
public participation in decision-making
processes related to the prevention of, and
response to, accidents involving hazardous
substances.

OECD Council Act
Decision on the exchange of information
concerning accidents capable of causing
trans-frontier damage

Standards

BRITISH STANDARDS INSTITUTION
Quality vocabulary
BS4778: 1991

Quality management and quality assurance
standards
BS EN ISO 9000: 1994

Total quality management
BS7850: 1994

Reliability of systems, equipment and
components
BS5760: 1994